THE SINS OF THE F

Have you ever wondered where your migraine came from?

Why are some girls compulsive nymphomaniacs?

What causes lack of confidence?

Why do some people grow fat?

Do false teeth cause sickness?

What causes frigidity or impotence?

Why will some men gamble the very shirt off their backs?

Also by the same author,
and available in Coronet Books:

The Curse of the Children

The Sins of the Fathers

Romark

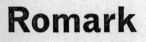

with a guest diagnosis by
Dr Bernard Levinson, MB, BCH, DPM
(President of the South African Society of
Clinical and Experimental Hypnosis).

CORONET BOOKS
Hodder Paperbacks Ltd., London

To my cousin, Dr Ray Antibe,
the only psychiatrist I have known to advise:
"Don't talk . . . Write!"

Printed and bound in Great Britain
for Coronet Books, Hodder Paperbacks Ltd.,
St Paul's House, Warwick Lane, London, EC4P 4AH
by Cox & Wyman Ltd.,
London, Reading and Fakenham

*The characters and situations in this book are based on true
occurrences but every attempt has been made to disguise them
without weakening the point of the story.*

ISBN 0 340 18870 7

Contents

Introduction: The Sins of the Fathers . . .

Theologically, the expression 'the sins of the fathers' has come to mean that the sins committed by parents must be expiated by their progeny, in some cases for many generations. This book presents another interpretation. Intelligent reading of the Scriptures points to the conclusion that they contain extremely adept psychology. The phrase 'the sins of the fathers' means surely that incorrect parental attitudes can create unhappiness and misery in the offspring and in the children's offspring for generation after generation.

Becoming a parent is the undertaking of an enormous responsibility. This book is concerned with sins—of commission and omission—by which children's lives can be ruined. In turn, children commit the same errors in bringing up *their* children. These mistakes and the miseries caused are propagated from generation to generation.

I have found in clinical work that more than ninety per cent of mental problems are created during the formative years—from birth to the age of seven. During that time children are under parental control—or are suffering the absence of parental control. The influences during this period dictate the entire course of their lives. So few parents realise that a child's instinctive attitude is to look up to them as perfect—infallible beings, Gods, all-knowing and all-powerful. It is only natural that this should be so. Children have no previous experience upon which to draw, enabling them to make comparisons and judgments. Parents are the main source of authority and wisdom.

As readers progress through this book they will find that all the case histories are different but in each instance the root cause is the same—parental influence.

The purpose of these volumes is threefold:

1. As a parent, you will be able to avoid snares and traps set by your own parents, which, if perpetuated by you, could easily be disastrous for *your* children.

It is terrifying that only an infinitely small percentage of parents who cause harm to their children wish to do anything but good. They sin, often grievously so, against their children without having any such intention.

2. Readers cannot fail to identify in some way with one or more of the characters. It is quite certain that they will be able to recognise members of their families, friends and acquaintances.

This should induce a more perceptive realisation of the working of the human mind and should, hopefully, create greater tolerance of human behaviour.

3. A third possibility is that a few old dogs, reading this book, understanding it and believing in it, will learn a few new tricks.

I have used an unusual format, a series of novellas (short novels) based on actual case histories. Names have been changed, the locations made vague and in some instances two or more cases have been combined in order to avoid repetition.

But every story is true.

This has been written primarily for the general reader, therefore the novella form has been chosen because it is easily assimilable by the lay public. For the same reason psychological terminology has been eliminated but trained professionals in the field of clinical psychology should find some of the treatments of interest.

Each history is followed by a Clinical Diagnosis, in which the events in the subject's life story are analysed. The reader is therefore a detective of psychology. The facts are presented in the novella and the reader's task is to anticipate the final disclosure in the Clinical Diagnosis.

Readers will probably divide into three groups:

1. Those who will simply read the novella as a story and accept the Clinical Diagnosis as part of it.

2. Those who will read the novella as a detective would, scanning for clues and red herrings, then arrive at the same conclusions as the writer, *before* they read the Clinical Diagnosis.

3. Those who reach entirely different answers—readers with their own theories ... which could of course be correct. My conclusions are not infallible.

This book is not a success story. Every chapter is taken from life. There are failures and partial failures.

The reader will find that clinical psychology is very like detective work, most of which is painstaking investigation, sometimes without result. There are no pat answers to every story. Sometimes there are no clues, therefore attempts to uncover truth reach a dead end. Sometimes success is nearly achieved—then the patient vanishes, never to return. Some people like to stay as they are and cannot live without their problems.

Sometimes there is an improvement, sometimes there is not. But there are one or two little miracles which seem to make everything worth while.

The more of these stories you read, the more knowledge you will gain of how the human mind works—just as I have learned by attending to these cases. Perhaps when you reach the end of the volume you will have acquired an understanding of basic psychology.

If this books prevents any parent from inadvertently ruining *any* child's life it will have served its purpose.

1: Clowns can get Headaches Too!

Agatha Bayliss stopped the sewing-machine and tilted her head, listening. She had heard no sounds from Franklin for at least half an hour. That meant he was up to something. He was a cheerful child and usually extremely noisy.

Agatha rose and set off ponderously in search of her eight-year-old son. She was a large woman with an enormous bosom. Her aged father had once told her approvingly: "Agatha, there can be no gainsaying that you are a significant woman. Significant."

Agatha's inspection of the house and grounds was perfunctory because she knew where Franklin was. In the attic. Nevertheless, she checked first because she didn't want to make the ascent to the roof unnecessarily. Agatha was practical and well-organised. She was fond of saying that she would rather have her feet on the ground than her head in the clouds.

There was no sign of Franklin. The attic it must be. Their house was old and in order to search the attic Agatha had to climb a narrow flight of wooden stairs. Although she was large, Agatha moved silently. She mounted the stairs until she could see through the aperture.

Sure enough, there was Franklin.

His thin legs were swallowed in an old pair of his father's riding boots. He had an unidentifiable garment, made of rich red brocade, swathed about his chest. Perched on his head was one of Agatha's grandmother's old hats—a feathered relic of another age.

Franklin was unaware of his mother watching him. He was lost in his world of imagination, muttering, gesticulating and stumbling about in the boots which covered his thighs.

Agatha's face hardened. She heaved herself into the

13

attic and Franklin noticed her for the first time. He stood in his fancy dress, looking at her with alarm.

"You're play-acting again, eh?" said Agatha, angrily. "If I've told you once I've told you a dozen times, Franklin, I do not approve of play-acting."

She walked to him and wrenched the hat from his head. She pulled the brocade from him and plucked him bodily out of the boots.

"Why can't you be satisfied with what you are?" she demanded. "Why do you always try to be what you're not?"

His voice piped: "I was doing the same as the pictures last night, Mummy!"

Agatha shook her head in exasperation. He had been to see 'The Three Musketeers'. That accounted for the boots and the feathered hat.

"You will stop this, once and for all," said Agatha.

Agatha did not believe in excessive physical punishment, but she did believe that a hiding should be administered when necessary, and that it should be memorable. Until now she had never felt obliged to beat her son. She spotted a brush in the corner and picked it up.

"Do you see this, Franklin?" she asked rhetorically.

The boy nodded, his eyes widening.

"I'm going to give you a thrashing with this, because you won't obey me. I've warned you before, but a warning is not enough."

She put him over her knee and gave him six sharp blows.

At first he was silent, then he began to cry.

Agatha put down the brush and looked at him.

"You must learn to be who you are. If you try to be someone else, you'll come to no good."

Agatha took her son by the hand and they left the attic together.

A year later, Agatha's sister, Bertha, came to dinner with her sixteen-year-old daughter, Felicity. Bertha lived in another part of the country and it was seldom that the sisters met. Felicity had not seen her aunt for ten years.

After dinner they moved to the lounge for coffee. Franklin, not yet tired enough to sleep, took up his favourite position on the well of the stairs, stretched out so that he could see without being seen. Every sound from the lounge Franklin could hear distinctly.

He lay there, drowsily, watching his mother, his father, his aunt and his cousin. Felicity's hair was shiny and black and she wore it in a long plait.

Reginald Bayliss poured himself a liqueur while the women sipped coffee. Reginald sat back, relaxed, and listened to the sisters' chatter.

"You seem happier about Franklin," said Bertha. "I've noticed from your letters."

"Really?" said Agatha. "Was it obvious before?"

"That you were worried? Oh yes! And if you don't mind me saying so I thought you were being over-cautious about the whole thing!"

"Over-cautious!" said Agatha, putting down her coffee cup. "You know why I'm worried! Franklin seems to have inherited all his Granny's failings."

"You mean fantasising," said Bertha.

"Play-acting, that's what it is. We don't need fancy words to explain it. It's an escape from life. Actors and actresses!" She snorted and poured more coffee.

"Oh come on, Agatha," said Reginald. "You've a fixation about actresses, haven't you."

"Well, can you blame me?" said Agatha. "Granny was an actress and look what became of her." She left the phrase hanging in the air.

"What did happen, Auntie?" asked Felicity, her curiosity aroused concerning her mysterious grandmother.

Agatha looked steadily at her sister.

"You haven't told her?" she asked accusingly.

"No," said Bertha. "I don't have the obsession about Granny that you have."

"I think it's irresponsible of you not to tell Felicity."

Reginald laughed. "Nonsense," he said. "You make her out to be a monster. She was just unfortunate."

15

Agatha looked at the young girl intently waiting.

"Your grandmother was an actress, with troupes which toured the country." She paused.

"Oh," said Felicity. "What happened to her?"

"She contracted syphilis and died in an asylum."

"Syphilis!" Felicity echoed the word as though it were a curse.

"Yes. And it was because she couldn't make her peace with reality. Play-acting! Actresses are a loose lot."

"Now come on, Agatha," said Reginald. "You're defaming a dead woman who was probably no better and no worse than millions of others. I rather like what I know of Grandma. Remember your mother's story about her?"

Agatha looked at her husband, trying to discourage the anecdote.

"I remember," said Bertha brightly. "It was when she was touring in the north and she knocked on the door of a boarding-house for accommodation.

"'What do you do?' asked the landlady.

"'I'm an actress,' said Gran.

"'Well I'm having no actresses here,' she said. 'You're all too highly sprung!'"

Reginald roared with laughter.

"That's it!" he said. "That's the one."

"There was nothing funny about her death," said Agatha darkly. "No comedy in that, was there?"

Bertha intervened as she saw signs of domestic trouble.

"Anyway, Agatha, you wrote that you nipped it in the bud, whatever that means ..."

"Yes," said Agatha. "I gave Franklin a thrashing and I've never caught him play-acting again."

Franklin shifted guiltily on the stairs.

Although Agatha curbed her son's 'play-acting', she did not eliminate his creative flair and during his teenage years it manifested itself in writing. Franklin wrote for the school newspaper and contributed articles to magazines. He was an intense, serious young man—yet his writing was distinctly humorous.

16

At university, Franklin became editor of the 'Rag' magazine, specialising in bawdy satire. In spite of all his mother's attempts to shield him from show-business, Franklin inevitably drifted into it. After graduation he joined a newspaper and began to specialise in reporting on entertainment. This type of journalist inevitably mixes with writers, producers, directors and performers. Encouraged by their interest, he wrote several comedy scripts and showed them around. Most of them were accepted.

Franklin—or Frankie as he was now known—found that doing what he liked most was providing him with a sizeable income. He left his journalistic job to concentrate on script writing. At first he wrote for radio. He cut his teeth as a professional writer while earning enough money to live. Then, as his talent developed, Frankie found that his scripts were being accepted more and more for television.

Within a few years Frankie had found his niche. He made good money, and he enjoyed himself. He mixed with stimulating people, personalities who entertained millions —with their talent—in front of the cameras and behind them.

One day Frankie was having lunch at the studio canteen with another young writer, Dave Lockhart. Dave specialised in drama, saying he was totally incapable of writing a funny line.

"I watched your show last night," said Lockhart, munching.

"How did you like it?" asked Frankie. He was always interested in Dave's opinion.

"Brilliant," said Dave. "I don't know where you get your ideas. There were a couple of lines which doubled me up."

Frankie looked at his friend with amusement.

"I've told you, Dave, there's nothing original in comedy. No, I'll re-phrase that. Inspiration does play a small part. But it's one part inspiration to nine parts perspiration. Comedy isn't an art, it's a science—as precise as mathematics."

"I don't believe it," said Dave with finality.

"It's true," said Frankie. "D'you know where I get my ideas?"

"No," said Dave.

"Half comes from my filing cabinet. The rest I steal."

Lockhart looked astonished.

"You don't mean it," he said.

"Of course I do. You see a comic and something he says or does strikes a note. You build on that beginning and finally you've found a new variation on an old theme."

"What about your filing cabinet?" asked Lockhart. He had only sold his first script a month previously. To him, Frankie was a veteran.

"I have thousands of gags cross-indexed. The best comedians have minds like filing systems. They test their audience in the first few minutes and find out what makes them laugh—then, they give it to them.

"Most people like to laugh at others' misfortunes—If a man slips on a banana peel, his dignity is shattered, so he looks ridiculous. Similarly, people laugh at idiotic faces."

Frankie was warming to his topic and Dave was a good listener.

"To be more sophisticated there's comedy in the illogical. Creating shocks by twisting commonplace situations."

Dave leaned forward and said: "But a lot depends on delivery, doesn't it? I couldn't tell a story and get anyone to laugh, but you can."

Frankie's attention was diverted by the arrival of Ron Maxted, a producer he wanted to meet.

Lockhart followed his gaze. "Oh," he said, "there's Ron."

"D'you know him?" asked Frankie.

"Sure."

"Do me a favour and introduce me."

Dave waved, caught Maxted's attention, and beckoned to him to come over.

It was a meeting which was to change Frankie's life. Maxted had been following Frankie's career with interest. They soon found that they were on the same wave-length and became friends.

A few months later, Maxted invited Frankie to join him in a provincial town where he was producing a show. After the performance they went to Maxted's hotel suite.

"Our advance man has laid on a few girls," said Maxted. "I can't say what they'll be like but he's usually okay."

Frankie said nothing. Other people's tastes infrequently coincided with his own. The advance man, Joe Philips, arrived soon after with three girls. They were bright, cheerful youngsters with good figures. Frankie looked them over, acknowledging Joe's introductions. Not for him, he decided.

Soon afterwards Maxted said: "You don't seem too happy about the girls!"

"I don't fancy them," said Frankie. "Hey, maybe Joe knows the receptionist. If he does, we'll invite her."

"You mean the thin bird behind the desk when we checked in?"

"That's the one," said Frankie.

"She's flat-chested," said Maxted.

"Exactly."

Joe knew the girl and she was happy to join them. Frankie soon had her charmed. Later, when members of the show arrived, it developed into an uproarious party. There were two comedians who began exchanging patter. Before long Frankie joined in.

Maxted went to the bar to replenish his drink and stood watching. There were about a dozen people seated in the lounge. Wisecracks flew, as Frankie and the two comedians exchanged lines. One comic would hit a laugh, like a sportsman playing a stroke, then the crowd would applaud with laughter.

Gradually the pattern changed. Only Frankie held the stage as the other comics dried up. Their stockpile of patter was finished, but Frankie's seemed inexhaustible. The spectators were still enthusiastic. They laughed and laughed, and Maxted observed how Frankie handled them. If they became hysterical he would slow them, then gradually pick them up once more.

Frankie's not a writer. He's a comedian. Realisation suddenly hit Maxted. Frankie should be performing, not grinding out brilliant material for second-rate comedians to ruin.

Ron was determined to do something about it. He brought up the subject on their way back to the capital.

"I was watching you last night, Frankie," he said.

"Eh? What d'you mean?"

"With the comics. You topped them every time."

"Yes? Well, they're pretty limited, aren't they?"

"No they're not. It's that you have an advantage over them. You have a comic's flair for delivery, but you also have a writer's brain and a mental filing system which won't let you down."

Frankie grinned, enjoying Maxted's flattery.

"Okay, if you say so!"

"I'm telling you, Frankie, you've got a future as a comic. Stop writing for other people. Write for yourself, and put it across yourself. You'll make the big time and the money!"

Maxted had the connections to create an opening for Frankie. Before the month was over Frankie was booked as a supporting act at a night club in the provinces. Maxted was in the audience for his début.

Frankie sat in the dressing-room, smoking nervously. Maxted had told him: "Go in and start. You'll soon feel at home."

Frankie had written four alternative patter acts for the show. He had learned the local slang and researched on local topics. He would follow a line of humour and if it did not take he would instantly switch to another. He knew that he would not fail. At the worst, the audience might hate him. But that he didn't mind.

Yet, emotionally, he was in a turmoil. He felt nervous and sick. He lit another cigarette. As he inhaled, he became nauseous. He stubbed it out. He heard the band play his introduction music. The compere made the announcement—then, he was 'on'.

He bounded on to the stage and launched into his patter. Immediately he felt the responsive waves of laughter.

He kept his mind calm as the laughter grew. He would deliver a line then wait for the laugh to break and reach a peak. As the laugh began to decline he would punch out another one-liner and the laughter would rise again. He felt power and confidence. While performing each laugh line, he was preparing others, shuffling them in his mind for future delivery.

"The town was so small the Rabbi was head of the Mafia."

"The girls were so ugly that when they held a beauty contest it lasted all year." Laughter.

"And nobody won." Laughter.

When he'd finished his ten-minute spot Frankie bowed off to rounds of applause, interspersed with appreciative whistles. He felt a surge of achievement. His mind had been sharpened by the stimulation of working to a live audience. He suddenly realised he was bathed in perspiration. To cool himself he splashed his face with cold water.

Maxted walked in, beaming.

"What did I tell you? You wowed them. You were *too* good. Some of the gags went over their heads." Maxted paused—"Yet I noticed something strange. You trained them to laugh at whatever you said. They couldn't believe that you would say anything that wasn't funny. So they laughed even when they didn't understand the joke. Amazing."

"Calm down, Ron," said Frankie, laughing. "No one's that good!"

"You are. You're not only good, you're great. Tonight was all I needed to see. You're on your way. We'll plan a programme of gradual exposure, put you on some of the guest shows and that should do it."

They went out to celebrate and after a good meal, had a lot to drink.

Frankie had an ex-girlfriend in town who had been to see the show. Now, she joined them.

"She's a beaut, isn't she?" said Frankie when he and Maxted were alone for a moment.

"Very pretty," said Maxted. "But I like them to curve. She's straight up and down, like a plank."

21

"She's got everything I need." Frankie gave a gesture of enthusiasm.

"To each his own," said Maxted, laughing.

Much later that night Frankie asked the others whether they'd like to watch a blue movie. They agreed and he went to his car to collect what he called his sex kit.

He had pornographic movies and collections of photos and sexual objects.

Frankie picked up a few of the sexual objects and started clowning with them. At first his girl-friend looked taken aback but then she began to laugh.

"You're funny," she said. "But funny peculiar, not funny ha-ha."

Frankie showed the film and Maxted and the girl agreed it was 'different'.

It was a triumphant evening, an occasion which he would remember as the launching of his new career—if Maxted could be believed.

When Frankie drove back to the capital the next morning he was haunted by a strange anxiety. He felt guilty without knowing what he had done wrong.

He started drinking at lunchtime and continued doing so all day. He went to bed extremely drunk.

The next morning he felt better, except for a slight headache. Maxted phoned to remind him that a script was due the next day. Frankie threw himself into his writing and felt fine.

During the next few months Frankie's career as a performer flourished. Maxted's influence was considerable, which created opportunities that an ordinary performer could never have achieved in so little time. Also, Frankie's own reputation as a comedy writer encouraged bookers to give him a chance. But the flattering thing, to Frankie, was that he was offered a return engagement at every venue.

"You're no flash in the pan, Frankie," said Maxted one night, when they were discussing future plans.

Maxted was a tall, gangly man. He wore his hair long and it hung over his eyes so that he was constantly brushing his hand across his forehead. The gesture made him seem nervous and ill at ease, which he never was.

"You've already become hot with the press," he told Frankie. "I had calls from two national Sundays today. They both want profiles of you for their colour magazines."

Maxted paced about the room excited by the prospects of Frankie's career.

"All in six months! And now you're really going to start, you'll be in the big money before next year. Think of it, Frankie! A thousand a week plus."

He paused and scrutinised Frankie, who was sitting silently.

"What's the matter? Does money depress you?"

Frankie laughed.

"Not at all. It's just that I don't believe any of this is happening. It's as though I'm living in one of my scripts." Frankie threw up his arms in exasperation. "Success can't come this easily, Ron! Can it?"

Maxted sat down next to Frankie, as though he could convince him by being closer.

"I've noticed that you're reacting oddly. Your success makes you glum!" Maxted laughed. "I know all comedians are weird but this is the first time I've heard of anyone being depressed because everything's going right." He glanced at Frankie and froze. The comedian was white-faced, his eyes hard.

Frankie spoke softly and deliberately.

"Don't give me that crap, Maxted. Keep your comments to yourself!"

"For God's sake, Frankie," said Maxted, genuinely upset. "I was only kidding around. What did I say, anyway?"

"Too much," said Frankie. He looked at his watch. "I'm on in ninety minutes. I want some time on my own."

"Sure," said Maxted. "I'll pick you up in an hour, right?"

When the producer was gone Frankie sat motionless, lost in thought.

He looked up and winced as the light from the overhead lamp caught his eyes. He put up his hand as a shield and went to a mirror to inspect his eyes. They seemed all right. There was nothing wrong that he could detect.

I hope I'm not getting another headache, he thought. He was working at the Zero Club tonight. Agents and producers would be there. It was vital that he be on top form. Frankie thought again of Maxted's words. Producers are all the same, he said to himself grimly. They think they own you.

"I feel like hell!" He began to rub the back of his neck. The muscles felt stiff and painful.

He went to the liquor cabinet and looked at the bottles. This was medicinal. He settled for a double brandy.

He knocked it back, neat. At once the warmth radiated from his stomach. Within minutes his mood changed. He felt better. To hell with all of them, he thought. He'd go on tonight and enjoy himself. They could book him or not. What did he care?

Frankie Bayliss worked well that night. One of the leading television 'talk show' hosts was in the audience and he asked Frankie to join him. The upshot was an appearance on the TV show two weeks later. Maxted's carefully planned programme knitted together. Frankie got break after break until he was so much in demand that Maxted could be highly selective about which dates to accept.

One afternoon he went to Frankie's new apartment. He had an offer which he knew would delight Frankie. It was for a movie. The money was good and Frankie would be working with people he liked.

He rang the bell. There was no reply. Funny, he thought. He'd spoken to Frankie on the phone at two o'clock and arranged to meet him at five. It was now 5.15. He rang again. Still no answer. Maybe he went out for a while, thought Maxted. Fortunately he had a key to the apartment. He and Frankie both kept irregular hours and he sometimes stayed overnight.

He let himself in. Everything was quiet. There was an

24

empty brandy bottle on the table. A glass was lying on the carpet. The smell of alcohol was everywhere. Maxted opened the windows, and then looked into the bedroom.

Frankie was sprawled on the bed, lying on his back, fully clothed. His mouth was open and a stream of spittle was running down his chin.

Maxted bent over him, then straightened.

"The bastard's dead drunk!" he said aloud.

Maxted took out his diary and consulted it. "It's an out of town engagement tonight. He's got to be sober by seven."

I'll let him sleep until six, he decided. He closed the door and tried to read a newspaper in the lounge, but he couldn't concentrate. He'd never seen Frankie in this state before. He'd noticed that Frankie was drinking a great deal lately. But that was normal in show business. The pressures were great, particularly for a comic of Frankie's quick-fire hard-hitting style. After each show he needed to unwind and the easiest way was with friends and a bottle. Now that Maxted ran Frankie's affairs full-time, they both lived a topsy-turvy life. They rose at lunchtime and went to bed at four or five in the morning—more often than not with a fair amount of drink in them.

Today's incident was out of character. Frankie must have demolished an entire bottle of brandy to be in his present state. Maxted shook his head. Frankie was still as contrary as ever to his personal success. The success was real. If Frankie needed proof all he needed to do was consult his bank balance.

At six o'clock Maxted went back into the bedroom. Frankie hadn't changed position but his breathing was quieter.

As he moved to the other side of the bed Maxted noticed Frankie's typewriter on the table. There was a sheet of paper in it and the beginnings of a script. The last line was a jumble of meaningless letters.

He's been trying to type, but was too drunk to hit the keys properly, thought Maxted. He was irritated by Frankie's persistence in writing scripts. It was a waste of time—and a waste of talent, thought Maxted. Frankie was still selling scripts to his old customers at normal fees.

With a negotiated deal Maxted could get him much more money.

Maxted brought his thoughts to the job at hand. He had to get Frankie sober enough to work that evening.

The comedian was still sodden with liquor and Maxted could not wake him. He lifted and propelled him around the room until he began to mumble in protest. Gradually Frankie came to.

Sitting on the edge of the bed, holding his head in his hands, eyes blood-shot, he groaned, "I feel like death!"

"Serves you damned well right," said Maxted. "For God's sake, what's got into you, getting potted in the middle of the day?"

"Why don't you go away and let me sleep," said Frankie, the words coming thickly.

"You've got a show tonight, remember? I don't understand you, Frankie. I arranged a week out for you, so you could relax. You're working flat out for the next three months, d'you realise that?"

Maxted pulled out the contract and waved it.

"This is an offer for a movie, and you've got co-star billing."

Frankie put out a hand to take the contract. He was shaking so much he could not grasp the document. It fell to the carpet. Frankie cursed and lurched for the lounge.

"Where're you going?"

"To have a drink."

Frankie picked up a bottle of brandy and a glass. He attempted to pour but his hands were shaking too much. He took the bottle in both hands, held it to his mouth and swallowed. Then he put the bottle down.

Maxted's reaction was astonished horror. Frankie wasn't just drunk—he was drinking like an alcoholic. Maxted watched the comedian in silence. Frankie regained some of his normal composure. The shaking diminished.

"You've really been on a jag," said Maxted.

Frankie gave a groan and fell back into a chair, stretching out his legs. He held the brandy bottle in his hand, his

26

fingers firmly around the neck as though it represented security.

"The last thing I want from you, Ron, is a lecture," said Frankie.

"And it's the last thing you'll get," said Maxted. "But what are you celebrating?"

Frankie took a swig from the bottle, coughed, and wiped his mouth with his hand. He held up the bottle.

"Without this, I couldn't have survived the last three months."

Maxted said nothing.

"I get headaches, you see," said Frankie, mystifyingly.

"What headaches?"

"Every time I work, I get them—odd headaches." Frankie stood, agitated, and walked to the other side of the room. He stood with his back to Maxted. "I can't stand bright lights. They pierce my eyes. And I get a ringing in my ears."

Frankie swung around.

"It's bloody terrifying. I feel I'm going blind. And . . ." Frankie paused. He couldn't get the word out.

"And what, Frankie," asked Maxted softly.

"And mad."

Fear appeared in Frankie's eyes. He put the bottle to his mouth and drank again.

Maxted put his arm round the comedian's shoulders.

"Why didn't you tell me before? For God's sake Frankie, that's what I'm here for! I could have called a doctor for you."

"I don't want a doctor," said Frankie, with force. "I've got the problem licked, don't you see?" he added with artificial brightness. He put the bottle down. Maxted thought: That's the first time he's let go of that bottle in fifteen minutes.

"I'm trying to explain that I get these neurotic attacks and when they are bad, they're bloody terrible. I know that I won't be able to go on. So I open a bottle and the heebie-jeebies disappear. Liquor is a guardian angel as far as I'm concerned."

27

Maxted said nothing. His mind was running ahead to the vital months of bookings and the tremendous amount of money involved. In spite of what Frankie had said, liquor very definitely had a hold on him. Maxted had seen this before. Hounded by fears, many people in show business sought solace in drink. It never worked.

"So liquor is your cure-all, eh Frankie?" he said.

"That's right," the comedian said, his eyes bright.

"I'm a realist, Frankie," said Maxted. "The next few months are important. If you have to drink to work, then drink. But I'll see to it that you don't drink too much. From now on I'm going to keep a phial of vitamin B12 with me. I'll give you an injection whenever I think you need one."

"What does that do?" asked Frankie, suspicious.

"It stops the alcohol destroying your liver and it helps to keep you sober."

"All right," said Frankie. He looked at the clock. "I'd better get ready."

"One more thing," said Maxted. "You're going to see my doctor tomorrow. These headaches could be caused by something quite simple. Perhaps you need glasses—could be anything."

Frankie agreed. That evening he judged his intake of alcohol well. He was in a mellow mood when he arrived at the out of town club.

A few minutes before he was due to go on he inspected the audience. They didn't have the sophistication of a big city crowd. They were raucous and he didn't like the look of them. He knew that to win over these morons he would have to resort to blue material, as dirty and obvious as possible.

The compere announced him and Frankie launched into his first line of patter. Within seconds he was in trouble. He tried another routine. There were isolated titters but that was all.

Progressively, Frankie's gags became lower and lower. He was now as smutty and as suggestive as he could be.

Even that didn't work. I'm dying, thought Frankie. For

the first time, I'm dying a death. It was a fate which every entertainer dreaded. To go on, do your best, and fail. 'Dying' was the professional term, and it couldn't have been more apt.

A drunk near the front had been staring belligerently at Frankie from the moment he came on. Now he stumbled to his feet and shouted: "Go home!" He waved his hands in the air and sat down again with a thud.

There was a roar of laughter from the audience. The heckler had succeeded, with his crude interjection, where Frankie's slick patter had failed. They were sadistic, Frankie realised. Eager to see the heckler destroy him.

Frankie surveyed the audience coolly, then focused on the heckler.

"Why don't you stand against the wall? That's plastered too," he said.

There was mild appreciation of this insult.

The heckler shouted something, but his words were indistinguishable.

"The last time I saw a mouth like that," said Frankie, "it had a hook in it."

A woman near the front found this 'ad lib' so funny that she began to laugh hysterically, a high-pitched shriek which quickly spread to the rest of the audience.

As though on cue, the drunk heckler stood up again, making inarticulate noises.

"Don't worry about the dummy, folks," said Frankie. "I work it with my foot."

Now the laughter was general. Frankie could sense victory.

He waited for another interjection from the heckler. When it came, he responded: "When that thing on your shoulders comes to a head, have it lanced!"

The crude insult pleased the audience and they went wild. They even began to applaud. The heckler stared at Frankie, comprehension slowly penetrating his alcoholic haze. He was being made a fool of.

"There's a bus leaving in ten minutes," said Frankie, flashing a grin at him. "Be under it!"

Finish when you're ahead, thought Frankie, and he made his exit to a storm of applause, whistles and shouts.

Pushing his way through the now cheerful crowd back to his dressing-room, Frankie thought: I was dying, then I stormed them with a handful of stock-in-trade put-downs. Ah well, that's show business!

The next day Frankie and Maxted visited the doctor. He listened quietly, with no expression of surprise.

"You're suffering from migraine, Mr Bayliss," he said. "It's a common complaint."

Frankie was astonished. He'd thought he was unique.

"Can you cure it?" he asked eagerly.

"There are many treatments," hedged the doctor blandly. "We'll have to see which proves most effective in your case."

He gave Frankie a thorough examination and warned him to moderate his drinking.

"Excessive consumption of liquor causes grave damage to internal organs, Mr Bayliss, and it can cause irreparable damage to the brain. If you get so drunk that you can't remember, then brain cells have been killed. Once destroyed, they cannot be resurrected." He gave Frankie a smile. "You *rely* on the swiftness of your intellect, don't you? I would advise you to avoid alcohol."

He gave Frankie some tablets to take whenever the migraine threatened, and asked him to let him know how he fared. If necessary, they could try other treatments.

When Frankie left the doctor's rooms he was scared, but also comforted. It was reassuring to know that he only had migraine. He'd thought he was going insane. On the other hand, the doctor's advice about alcohol worried him. Everything depended on the medicine. He knew, now, that migraine was a common complaint, but that didn't make it any more bearable.

That same evening Frankie was to appear on a national television show. The doctor had given him a massive dose of B12 and advised him to eat. Dutifully, Frankie went home, ate a steak and spent the afternoon relaxing.

At 4.30, he was lying with his hands behind his head, in a meditative mood. He thought: I haven't had a drink all day. Maybe I'll have just one. To prove I can take it or leave it. No, he thought, better not. He glanced out of the window. It was clouding over, getting dark. He got up, put on the lights and as he did so he felt a pang.

He put his hand to the base of his neck and massaged the muscles. They were painful. Oh God, he thought. Not again! He looked at the light and at once his eyes twinged. He looked askance at the globe. To have looked at it openly would have created excruciating pain. With the onslaught of his migraine, it was as though a curtain had been drawn over his peripheral vision.

Frankie took the tablets the doctor had prescribed and lay down again, waiting for the formula to work.

He felt drowsy but apart from that, there was no perceptible effect. The migraine became worse. He was aware of strange sounds, half-heard ringings, like artificial bells. He put his hands to his ears. It's never been so bad, he thought. And the tablets don't help. He lunged across the room and seized a bottle of brandy.

Thirty minutes later Frankie was half-drunk. The migraine had subsided. His eyes throbbed slightly, but not enough to be disturbing. Frankie sprawled across the settee, a glass in his hand. Brandy ... the best medicine, he thought, with inane alcoholic humour.

He put down the glass and was about to pour from the bottle when he thought better of it. If he could stay exactly like this, he'd be all right tonight. I'll have one brandy every thirty minutes, he decided. That should do it.

He thought about Maxted. Maxted wouldn't like it. Maxted didn't mind him getting smashed after the show, but not beforehand. He would drink unobtrusively. He went to the liquor cabinet and found what he was looking for. Half a dozen miniature bottles. He emptied them, then carefully filled them with brandy, making sure that each small bottle was full to the brim. Each miniature held two tots. He distributed the bottles—two in the suit he was

31

wearing and four in the suitcase he planned to take with him the next day.

He felt fear. Six wasn't enough. He needed more miniatures. But he was pleased with himself for having thought of such a simple solution. Frankie remembered the doctor's advice—Eat. He looked at his watch. Six p.m. He didn't feel hungry. He'd eat after the show.

Ron Maxted came at 7 p.m. As far he could see Frankie was in good shape. He had obviously had a few drinks, but would be all right.

They made their way to the television studio and in the guests' lounge they were offered drinks. Maxted took a whisky but to his amazement Frankie refused.

"Not now thanks," said Frankie, and winked at Maxted.

That's my boy, thought Maxted. That talk with the doctor did the trick.

Five minutes later Frankie went to the toilet, entered a cubicle, took out a miniature bottle, unscrewed the cap and carefully drank exactly half of it. The neat brandy made him cough. He took out a packet of breath-fresheners and popped one in his mouth.

When he rejoined Maxted he was in good humour. During the show he was ebullient, incisive and totally in control.

As he came off Maxted clapped him on the back.

"That's the way I like it! The *old* Frankie Bayliss."

They went to a late night restaurant for dinner. Frankie drank too much wine but Maxted didn't mind. He deserved to enjoy himself, after the way he'd pulled himself together.

The audience were laughing too much. An over-responsive audience is as bad as a hostile one, thought Frankie, watching the happy faces. They ruin your timing and they interrupt the continuity.

Frankie was working at the Cosmo Club in the heart of the city. It was patronised by such an unpredictable audience that no entertainer ever knew what to expect from them.

Tonight, they'd been beautiful. From the moment he came on Frankie knew they liked him. Audience approval is something an entertainer can sense and Frankie had this audience in the palm of his hand.

Curiously, Frankie wasn't enjoying himself. He felt ill at ease. He thought: I'll liven things up.

An elderly woman had left the room previously, obviously to go to the toilet. Frankie had refrained from cracking the obvious gag about her destination. Now he saw her returning. She was about sixty with a friendly face.

He waved at her and she waved back, shyly.

"Could you hear me out there?" he asked.

"Why yes," she said.

"Because we could hear you," said Frankie. He didn't smile when he uttered the words. There was silence. The elderly woman looked surprised and sat down. The people at her table bent over and whispered.

I'm playing games, thought Frankie. A veteran comic had once told him: "It's not what you say, it's how you say it." Frankie had just proved him right. He'd turned a bantering gag into an insult.

But Frankie was enjoying himself. He directly antagonised a fat man by making explicit reference to his gross overweight. Frankie felt the atmosphere change. The audience which had loved him five minutes ago was now hostile.

"Come on," said Frankie, his voice harsh. "Why don't you hold hands and try and contact the living."

He kept it up for another five minutes. By then, he had alienated the entire audience. All they had wanted was to sit back in comfort, enjoy their drinks, and be amused. Now Frankie had shocked them into a mood of hatred. They resented him and they made it obvious.

Frankie stood in the spotlight, looking slowly around the room. There was an unbroken onrush of verbal hostility. If he had spoken, they wouldn't have heard him. People were standing, shouting and gesticulating, hissing and indicating their disapproval in every way.

The compere came on stage and took Frankie by the arm.

"You maniac," he whispered. "What do you think you're doing? Get off for Christ's sake!"

Frankie grinned and sauntered off nonchalantly. Then impulsively he dashed back on stage and stood with his arms widespread in the traditional gesture of an artist accepting acclamation.

The compere looked on horrified.

Frankie stood interminably, bowing, nodding and throwing his arms wide. Confused, the audience stopped booing and soon the room was silent. But Frankie refused to leave the stage. He kept it up, relentlessly, acknowledging non-existent applause.

Eventually the manager and the compere came on and between them they forced him off the stage. From the audience, there was an embarrassed silence.

"What the hell do you think you're doing!" said the manager, his eyes blazing with rage.

"Enjoying myself," said Frankie, and laughed at the confusion he had created among those dolts in the audience.

No one shared Frankie's amusement.

Six months later Frankie woke up one morning feeling that something was wrong. He had a hangover. He peered at the window. It looked strange. Different.

This isn't my room! The realisation hit him and he sat bolt upright in bed. Somebody moaned next to him. He looked down. It was a woman. A dyed blonde of about forty. The roots of her hair were brown.

Where am I? Who's this ugly cow next to me? Afraid that he would awaken her, he slipped out of bed. As his feet touched the floor his head throbbed with pain.

I must have really laid one on last night, he thought. Whisky ... that was the reason, he decided. Never mix your drinks. He saw his trousers and hurriedly pulled them on, trying to remember the previous evening.

Although he tried, he could not recall ever having seen

the woman in the bed before and he had no idea where he was. The last memory he had was dining with Maxted and two girls at a restaurant. That must have been about 1 a.m. Then one of the girls suggested they go to a discotheque, which he'd thought was bloody silly. From then on, the night was a complete blank.

When he had dressed he looked out of the grimy window. He was in a walk-up flat in a slum district.

Frankie went out of the apartment and closed the door quietly behind him.

I need a drink, he thought. He was trembling with the compulsion for alcohol.

I've got the shakes. Where am I going to get a drink at this hour? It was 8.30 a.m. He felt in his pockets for money. Nothing! He remembered the miniatures. He fumbled eagerly in his pockets and produced the tiny bottles. They were both empty. He opened them and sucked out the drops they contained. Not enough to tingle his tongue.

He thought desperately. The prospect of not being able to have a drink soon was terrifying. Without a drink he would die. Dread descended on him. Fear made his heart beat faster and his sweat glands overworked.

Oh my God! The words were a silent scream of agony. Pull yourself together, he commanded himself and went through his pockets again. He had his cheque-book with him. That was a stroke of luck. He could get to his bank in about fifty minutes if he walked. They opened at 9.30. If only I can hold out until then, he thought. He'd cash a cheque, buy a bottle at a liquor store and take a cab home. He couldn't think of a quicker way to get himself organised.

He started to walk. His gait was unsteady and he had difficulty in controlling his legs. They moved spasmodically and he couldn't keep on a straight line. He kept swerving to the side.

The cold air of the morning cleared his head but made him feel faint. Don't pass out! he commanded himself. You can't get a drink until you cash a cheque. He kept walking.

Eventually he saw the bank's sign half a block away. He thought: How am I going to sign the cheque? He walked

35

into the bank and sat in the lounge area. There were no other customers there. The bank had just opened.

He took out his cheque-book and let it drop on the table in front of him. It was easier than trying to put it down, because he had the shakes so badly, he might hurl it across the room. He placed both hands on the table to keep them still. Cautiously he reached for the pen, attached to the centre of the table.

He glanced at the row of tellers. A teller caught his eye and called: "Good morning, Mr Bayliss!"

Now they'll all look, thought Frankie despairingly. They did, registering that they had a celebrity in the bank.

Frankie got up and sat in the seat opposite the one he had been occupying. Now he had his back to the row of clerks. When he had the shakes it was difficult for him to sign his name. When people watched him, it became impossible.

He waited a few moments, then essayed a hurried signature. It ran off the side of the cheque in a splotch of ink.

He ripped out the cheque and crumpled it into his pocket. He needed a drink now, this instant, but he wasn't going to make a complete fool of himself in front of a row of bank clerks. He impulsively walked out of the bank and round the block, hoping that the exercise would quell his jumpiness. It took him ten minutes to circumnavigate the block and when he went into the bank again he was blowing hard and his hands were cold.

He sat down again with the cheque book.

He stared at the cheque with determination and in a flash of movement, penned his signature. He studied it. It looked wild, but it would do. Then he wrote the rest of the cheque. Strangely, he was able to write quite legibly. It was only his signature that caused trouble.

Wearily he took the cheque to the counter.

Smiling, the teller took it from him and stamped it. Then he paused, gazing at the slip of paper.

"I'm sorry Mr Bayliss," he said, "but the cheque is torn. It must have ripped when you took it from your book. Would you endorse it, please." He leaned forward conspiratorially. "We have a finicky accountant." He pushed the cheque back to Frankie. "How do you want it?" he asked.

"In fives," said Frankie. He thought: I've got to sign it again and this time right in front of him.

Desperate, Frankie said: "Why do those women gossip instead of working?"

The teller, surprised, looked over his shoulder. As he did so, Frankie signed the torn cheque. When the teller turned back to him, Frankie had the cheque ready.

He took the money and walked out. When you're a drinker, he thought, small things can make life hell.

He bought a bottle and in the taxi opened it and took a long pull. He began to feel better.

Maxted was waiting in his apartment when he arrived.

"Where the hell did you get to?"

"You tell me!" said Frankie. "I woke up in bed with some broad I'd never seen before." He shuddered at the remembrance. "What happened last night anyway?" He had no idea what had happened but he was certain he was in some kind of trouble.

Maxted looked thoughtful.

"Maybe it's better I don't remind you."

Frankie sat down despairingly. "Is it that bad?"

"You say you don't remember what happened. What *can* you recall?"

Frankie thought. His memory did not extend beyond the point at which the girl had suggested the visit to a disco. He told Maxted so.

"That's right, Sheila said let's go to a disco," said Maxted.

"So what happened after that?" said Frankie, pouring a drink. He felt so bad he didn't care about Maxted seeing him drinking.

"Jesus," said Maxted. "Brandy for breakfast! Anyway, after she suggested the disco, you flipped. You said she was stupid and that the only reason she wanted to go to the discotheque was because she didn't have brains enough to carry on a conversation. She said you were a lush, so

37

you threw your drink at her. Then you walked out, and presumably got yourself picked up."

Frankie sat huddled, his face averted.

Maxted's voice hardened: "You're slipping, Frankie. You were lousy last night. Your timing was shot. You fluffed words. You looked drunk, which you were. But it's after the show that's beginning to count. You've made too many ugly scenes. Clubs are beginning to cancel your bookings."

Maxted sat next to him. "Look at me, Frankie. You can't run away from responsibility all your life. You've a great career going and you're screwing it up completely. What for? Do yourself a favour and cut out the booze!"

Frankie pulled himself free of Maxted's grasp.

"That's a bloody bright suggestion, I must say!" He faced Maxted. His face was contorted by fears and insecurities. "Look at me! I'm like a machine that won't run without petrol. Fill me with brandy and I tell funny stories."

"Not any more, you don't," said Maxted bitingly. "The fuel doesn't work any more."

Frankie looked at his friend pathetically.

"But I don't know how to stop. And if I do stop, the migraine will drive me mad!"

CLINICAL DIAGNOSIS

Frankie's intake of liquor had reached such proportions that he began to experience all the manifestations of alcoholism, anxiety attacks, uncontrollable shaking of the hands and memory loss. Liquor was also beginning to damage his physique to a serious degree.

Alcohol is a depressant which temporarily decreases anxiety and induces a mild sense of euphoria. Frankie Bayliss used it as a psychological crutch, to ward off migraine and his concomitant fears of blindness and lunacy.

Frankie's problems began with his mother.

As a child he was imaginative and creative. Most children are instinctive actors. Fantasy enchants them and it is natural to 'play-act'.

Frankie had a well-developed creative drive and he liked to dress up for the roles he invented, imitating and elaborating upon what he had seen at the cinema.

But his mother, Agatha, had developed a morbid fear of acting because her grandmother was an actress in the days when theatre people were considered disreputable. Grandmother contracting syphilis and dying in an institution were, to her, direct outcomes of her being an actress.

She did not consider that in those days there were no antibiotics and that syphilis was difficult to cure. She paid no heed to the fact that distinguished people in all walks of life had succumbed to the same illness.

Agatha's equation was: play-acting equals insanity and death.

When she found Frankie pretending to be a musketeer in the attic, she physically punished the child. As he had never been beaten before, this emphasised the degree of his shock.

Agatha exhorted him to "Be what you are, don't try to be someone else, or you'll never come to any good."

This admonition was fixed in Frankie's mind a year later when he eavesdropped on a conversation in the lounge. He heard his mother talking about play-acting, syphilis and insanity.

His mother's obsession infected him.

Play-acting, 'Not being oneself', became linked with insanity and hideous sickness—his mother's warped equation of dementia and death.

Frankie's creative qualities could not be suppressed however, and he sublimated his artistic urges in writing. If Frankie had remained a writer, in all probability his life would have proved successful and uneventful.

Ron Maxted happened on the scene and was perceptive enough to realise that Frankie Bayliss had a creative facet far more remunerative than script writing.

He encouraged him to become a performer. He became a famous comedian.

But Frankie Bayliss's subconscious was unhappy about this. Frankie's own conception of his persona was as a writer, not an actor. There is a world of difference between the two. A writer is behind the scenes, an actor is in the limelight.

Frankie thought of his career as 'play-acting'. His first performance on stage as a comedian was a triumph. Yet, the next day, his subconscious lacerated him with guilt. He felt intense anxiety without apparent cause.

Logically, in terms of the principles instilled in Frankie by his mother, 'play-acting' must inevitably be followed by retribution in the form of guilt, insanity, and finally death. This guilt-induced anxiety created physical tension.

Tension manifested itself in Frankie by knotting the muscles at the base of his neck. This created a constriction of the blood supply to the brain and the optic nerves.

Frankie became hypersensitive to light and his eyes began to pain. As the blood supply to the brain was now pressurised because of the muscular tension he heard ringing sounds in his head.

These were physical manifestations, induced by a muscular tension of psychosomatic origin. But to Frankie's highly developed imagination the symptoms meant that he was going blind or mad. The dreaded consequences of his 'play-acting' were becoming reality.

His irrational fear of insanity was reflected in his angry reaction to an innocent remark by Maxted. The producer had said: "I know all comedians are weird but this is the first time I've heard of anyone being depressed because everything's going right." The word 'weird' touched Frankie on a raw nerve of fear.

To escape from the frightening symptoms of migraine, Frankie took to alcohol. At first it had the required effect, reducing his anxiety and therefore muscular tension. But the cure became more dangerous than the ailment.

Maxted's doctor correctly diagnosed Frankie's complaint as migraine but did not attempt to probe beyond that. The tablets he prescribed proved less effective than Frankie's own remedy, alcohol, so Frankie reverted to drink.

At the beginning of his career as a comedian, Frankie 'insured' himself by continuing with his writing. But he eventually stopped and his escape valve was closed. Gradually, Frankie developed the drinking habits of an alcoholic. He began to drink furtively. Consumption of liquor was no longer pleasurable, it was deadly serious. When he drank, he didn't sip. He poured it down.

Not having a drink within reach in case he 'needed' it, undermined his security. He believed that he could not live without alcohol. And yet the alcohol would have finally killed him if the pattern had been allowed to continue. He thought of alcohol as a friend—it was his most deadly enemy. Frankie's deep sense of guilt created a self-destruction which became manifest on the cabaret floor.

An example was his perverse behaviour toward two typical audiences. The first audience didn't like him. They thought him unfunny and did not respond. He was a failure. This did not upset Frankie, however, because he secretly believed that he did not deserve to be on a stage, entertaining people. He was therefore calm and detached. When the drunken heckler joined in, Frankie demolished him verbally—and paradoxically won his audience.

Conversely, when he appeared at the Cosmo Club and the audience adored him, Frankie was driven by his self-destruction to antagonise them. And he succeeded.

Frankie's attitude to sex was typical of professional comedians. He was fascinated by bizarre sex. He had a 'sex-kit' of pornographic film and other objects.

Most comedians start their professional careers as impressionists. They put on other accents and personalities like cloaks. They do not know who they really are and for this reason are often confusingly un-funny off stage. In fact, comedians in private life are usually serious people—often morose.

Frankie, like other comedians, thought people liked him best when he was being funny even in his sexual activities.

41

The girlfriend who said he was 'funny-peculiar' hit the nail on the head. Frankie had a sex-kit because he felt he had to be ready for anything in bed.

Frankie's mother had been domineering and her interference with his fantasy life rankled. His subconscious hatred of his mother manifested itself in his adult life in his antipathy toward women with developed breasts. Although heterosexual, Frankie sought flat-chested girls.

An illuminating insight into Frankie's dilemma was provided by the difficulty he had in signing his name on the cheque when he was desperate for a drink. Although his hands were shaking badly, Frankie only had trouble with his signature. He easily managed to fill in the rest of the cheque. Frankie equated his signature with giving autographs to fans. An autograph is a specific assertion of success as a performer—the very thing his subconscious mind was opposed to. As a result his mind balked.

Frankie's hands shook almost uncontrollably at times because of the enormous quantities of liquor he was consuming. As soon as the liquor wore off, Frankie began to shake. Although liquor caused the shakiness, it could also cure it. In fact it was the only instant cure. This encouraged Frankie to regard drink as a panacea. After all, what else could stop the shakiness? But it was a deception, for the cure was only temporary, and the shakiness would resume to remind him that he needed a further drink.

Frankie responded well to the laying bare of his childhood. As he began to understand himself, and was no longer driven by irrational fears, he was able to bring his liquor consumption down. But by ordinary standards Frankie still drinks excessively. He was also able to expurgate his guilt about being a performer, rather than a writer. Now he combines both roles.

Frankie's mother's well-intentioned desire to protect her son from the disastrous consequences of a life on stage very nearly destroyed him.

2: If You're Fat and Happy
   You'll Die Laughing

George and Mary Brown were entertaining friends, a young married couple like themselves. Dorothy and Roger Martin had brought their baby son with them and he lay now in his carry-cot in a bedroom. He had just begun to cry, an insistent sound which jarred their nerves.

Dorothy looked at the cot in the corner of the lounge where Judy Brown lay, quiet and content.

"I don't know how you do it, Mary," she said. "Every time we visit you I feel envious. Judy is so well behaved. Our boy makes enough noise to wake the neighbourhood but Judy is always so happy. One day you must let me in on the secret."

Dorothy went to the bedroom to attend her crying baby.

Mary smiled at her husband, then at Roger. When Dorothy came back into the room she said: "You're right, Dorothy, we do have a secret."

Dorothy laughed. "Tell me! what is it?"

"Judy isn't so well behaved. Before you arrived she was squalling like anything. But I've found a way to stop it. I simply shove a bottle of milk in her mouth. After that, nothing seems to bother her."

"Live and learn," sighed Dorothy. "I must take a leaf out of your book."

One day some years later, Judy Brown, now a cute little girl with blue eyes and golden blonde hair, was taken by her mother on a shopping expedition. It was just before Christmas and the shops were full of decorations and wonderful presents.

Judy stopped outside a display window and tugged at her mother's hand. There, in front of her, was the most beautiful doll she had ever seen. It was electric and its eyes lit and moved. It could even manipulate its arms and legs. Judy's mother, bending over her three-year-old daughter, could see how entranced the little girl was.

"Can I have it, Mummy?" asked Judy.

Mary's heart went out to her. How could she refuse?

"All right, Judy," she said. "You can have it for Christmas."

Judy was so excited she went to sleep especially early every night, so that the next day would come a little sooner.

On the morning of Christmas Day, Mrs Brown checked the living-room to see that everything was in order. The Christmas tree was a sparkling reminder that this was the festive season. Judy's presents were in neat little parcels.

She and her husband, George, fetched Judy from her room and the trio sat on the carpet and began the age-old ritual of families everywhere on Christmas Day.

"Where's my doll, Mummy?" asked Judy.

Mary and George Brown exchanged a concerned glance. How could they explain to their child that the doll had been too expensive? Mary Brown had read somewhere that children, even at an early age, appreciate an honest answer.

"We couldn't get the doll for you, Judy," she said. "It was terribly expensive and we found our budget couldn't cover it." The words were meaningless to Judy. She was crying bitterly. It was her first major disappointment.

"Look, darling," said her father helplessly. "Look at all these lovely presents," and he tried to distract her attention. But Judy had been dreaming of her doll for a week. Her mother had promised. How could her mother lie to her?

Mrs Brown looked at the weeping little girl. Why had she promised the doll so impulsively? Children took everything so seriously.

She began to open the parcels for Judy. Gradually the little girl's attention was drawn to the presents. George had a brainwave. He went to the sideboard and came back with a Christmas stocking stuffed with miniature chocolates.

He thrust the stocking into Judy's hand. "There, darling," he said. "Have some of these."

44

The child opened the stocking and began to pop choco-lates into her mouth. Soon the tears were gone.

George stood with his arm around his wife. "We'll get her that doll," he said. "We'll cut a few corners and manage somehow."

"Of course we will," said Mary. "She's taken it quite well. Children have such short memories, but it was foolish of me to promise her something I wasn't sure we could afford."

Judy was a pleasant child. No tantrums, fits of temper or jealous rages. She looked at the world through friendly, soft-hearted eyes. Perhaps, because of this, when Judy *was* naughty, her parents were shocked.

George came home from work one evening and, as he closed the front door, sensed that something was wrong.

Mary told him that she had been horrified, only a few minutes earlier, to find Judy trying to pull the cat's whis-kers.

"I gave her a smack," she told George. "But I'm not sure whether she understands that she mustn't torment animals."

George looked at his daughter. She sat quietly and apprehensively, a sad little girl with tear-smudged cheeks. He knew he must show his disapproval. There was an open packet of chocolate cream biscuits on the table. He, his wife and Judy always had some with their tea. He knew Judy loved them.

"You've been a naughty girl," said George, in his sternest voice. Judy looked at him with frightened eyes. She'd never heard that tone before from her father. Didn't he love her any more?

George walked to the table, picked up the biscuits, took them to the cupboard and locked them away. "No biscuits for you tonight," he said. "You must learn not to make animals unhappy or hurt them."

Judy was overwhelmed. First her mother had smacked her, then her father was nasty, now her favourite biscuits were being taken away.

She looked so unhappy that it wasn't long before her father began to feel sorry for her. After dinner he looked questioningly at his wife. She smiled. "All right," she said.

George unlocked the biscuits and gave Judy her treat before she went to bed. The incident was closed.

Judy grabbed her satchel and dashed to her mother for a kiss before she went to school.

Mary gave her daughter a hug and patted her on the head.

"Go along or you'll be late." She handed Judy her lunch box. Judy didn't enjoy the lunches provided by the school so Mary now made up a good nourishing meal for Judy to take with her.

Judy took the box but hesitated as though her mother had forgotten something. She looked questioningly at Mary.

"Oh yes, poppet, I'm sorry." She'd forgotten to give Judy her bar of chocolate. Judy grabbed the chocolate and ran out of the front door, unwrapping the paper from the bar.

Judy had no problem adjusting at school. She was pretty, outgoing and made friends easily. One day she came home in tears. Her mother was aghast.

"What's the matter, Judy?" she asked.

"They called me Fatty," said Judy. "One boy said I was a baby hippo." She burst into tears again.

"Is that all?" said Mrs Brown, laughing. "You're not a fatty, darling." She looked at her daughter. "You're a little plump, but that runs in the family. Your father's side and mine. We're all a little over-weight, but it doesn't matter. Haven't you heard the saying: Fat people are happy people?"

Mary Brown returned to the kitchen, where she had been preparing a four-course dinner. George had just been promoted and she wanted to surprise him.

That evening before she went to bed, Judy took off her clothes and studied herself in the full-length mirror. What Mummy had said was true, she *wasn't* a Fatty. Maybe she was roly-poly, but if it ran in the family, there wasn't anything she could do about it. She went down to the kitchen and had several slices of bread and jam to cheer herself up.

Some years later, Judy made her first effort to lose weight. She was now a teenager, and she and her friends were becoming conscious of cosmetics, clothes and boys. Their figures had become important.

By now, Judy's basically good shape had become considerably inflated. She may not have deserved 'fatty' in the past, but she certainly warranted it now. Judy chose a recommended diet and followed it faithfully. In the first week she lost a few pounds, but then, inexplicably, the rate of weight-loss slowed. She felt faint and curiously depressed most of the time. She found it difficult to concentrate. This was a major problem because she should have been doing heavy swotting for her school examinations.

After three weeks she weighed herself again. She had lost hardly any weight at all. Depression overtook her. To go through all that unhappiness and deprivation only to lose a few measly pounds which didn't make her look any different! In the seclusion of her room she burst into tears. Again she took off her clothes in front of the mocking mirror.

"Fatty!" she said derisively. "Fatty ... and you're stuck with it!"

She dressed, ran to the kitchen and prepared a feast. With the act of preparation her spirits lifted. She became elated. When her parents came in she laughed and joked with them. This was Judy at her warmest and most lovable.

In her bed that night, gorged and temporarily satiated, Judy thought of her futile efforts to fight her weight problem. "I'm going to be fat for the rest of my life," she said to herself. The tears welled and she cried herself to sleep.

A few months later Mary took Judy to buy a dress for the school dance. Judy had been talking about the dance for weeks and Mary wanted her to look her best. She had her own affectionate memories of school dances. To a teenager they were very important.

When they reached the shop, Mary was impressed by the choice of colours and styles. The new trends were bright and original.

"Look at this, Mum," called Judy. Mary went over to see what her daughter had found.

It was stunning. Mary held it up to examine it.

"It's a Junior Miss, darling," she said. "Size eight. Too small for you."

"Oh darn, so it is," said Judy, disappointed.

Mary followed her daughter as she tried dress after dress. But Mary soon realised that all the teenage dresses were either tens or twelves. Judy tried a few times to force herself into a twelve, but it was impossible.

Eventually the assistant made a suggestion. "I really don't think we have anything in the juvenile range which will fit your daughter. Shall we look among the ladies' dresses?"

Eventually they chose a dress which fitted Judy perfectly. It was drab but Mary promised Judy she'd make some changes.

"I'll give it a bit of colour darling, and you'll look terrific."

Judy looked at the dress without enthusiasm. It was 'middle-aged' and she would have to wear it at the dance!

On the night of the dance Judy sat glumly watching her friends. No one asked her to dance all evening. It was a relief when she was finally able to go home.

Although she was now considerably over-weight, Judy had a charming and relaxing personality. She gave affection generously and was easy to love. She was a superb cook and had a maternal warmth which appealed to many men. She had plenty of boyfriends, but they were friends rather than lovers.

One night she was invited to a party and met Tom. He was a jolly giant of a man, over-weight like herself. They got on famously. She and Tom were the fattest people present and it wasn't long before they took the party over. They did an impromptu barber-shop routine together and a hilarious version of the can-can which nearly demolished the furniture.

She and Tom had much in common, apart from over-weight. He too had a gentle disposition. He soon proposed to her and she accepted. They led a contented married life and Tom seemed to enjoy his wife being 'half a ton of fun', as he described her. Tom was a trencherman—a man who really enjoyed his meals. Judy derived a great deal of pleasure from preparing dishes which they could both enjoy.

Soon after their wedding Judy became pregnant. Like many young women she had always had mixed feelings about pregnancy. Now, to her surprise, she found that she loved it. She flaunted her condition wherever she went, making no effort to conceal herself in maternity outfits. Somehow, carrying the baby, Judy no longer had the feeling of being over-weight.

Judy had a trouble-free labour but she was upset to discover afterwards that she had gained weight considerably. As soon as she could, Judy became pregnant again. She and Tom had decided to have a family of three. Her second child was another boy.

"Come on, Judy," said Tom banteringly one evening. "You still haven't done your duty. Let's have a daughter."

So Judy became pregnant for the third time. Mornings were the busiest time of her day, tending to the youngsters and the house. But after lunch she usually found herself bored and she would drive to the nearest shop and look for something to read.

Judy's pregnancy proceeded without any complications and, as she and Tom had wished, this time it was a girl. Soon after her return from the nursing home, Judy followed her custom and went to the nearby shop. She bought some magazines and two boxes of chocolates. As she was paying for her purchases the owner of the shop gave her a smile. He was a friendly old gossip.

"When is it due, Mrs Brown?" he said, with a glance. "Must be any day now, eh?" He handed her the change.

Judy looked at the shopkeeper, stunned. Then she blurted out: "I had the baby three weeks ago." She turned and walked off leaving an embarrassed silence behind her.

Judy drove home and parked the car. She went into the lounge and sat on the sofa. Her mind was still spinning from the unintended insult. She began to weep and it was a long time before she stopped crying. Judy sat, feeling sorry for herself, eating chocolates from the boxes she had bought. Eventually she felt for a peppermint cream but the box was empty.

That's impossible, she thought. I bought two boxes. She looked at the carpet. There were the two boxes—empty. Judy had a moment of self-perception which horrified her. She looked at the clock. She had guzzled two full boxes of chocolates in less than half an hour.

She rose and waddled to the bathroom where she examined herself in the mirror. She was gross. Year after year she had added pound after pound. Now, she was as enormous as a fat lady in a circus. I'm not a complete fool, she thought in savage self-derision. Tom hasn't come near me for more than a year. He probably can't bear the idea of wrestling with this great mass of flab. Every time we go out I notice his eyes following other women—as long as they're slender. My marriage is on the rocks. I'm fat, unhappy and life isn't worth living.

Judy began to sob again, hopelessly, despairingly, until her eyes were puffed and her features distorted. Why am I cursed like this, she thought. Must I be fat and horrible and obscene all my life? What have I done to deserve it?

CLINICAL DIAGNOSIS

Nearly every parent is guilty of creating future weight problems in their children. Most people, fortunately, escape the traps so innocently set. Many do not. Judy Brown was one of the unfortunates.

Judy's eating problem started in early infancy. To keep

Judy quiet, her mother slipped a bottle of milk into her mouth. Later, came Judy's first major disappointment when her parents did not buy her the present they had promised for Christmas. When she did not receive the doll she expected she was desperately unhappy. To relieve that unhappiness, her father gave her chocolates. The mental association was established—unhappiness can be turned into happiness by eating sweets.

Conversely, when Judy misbehaved, she was punished by having sweets withheld from her. The association was reinforced—*not* having sweets was synonymous with being unhappy. Judy's parents had unconsciously used the reward-and-punishment system by giving or withholding food.

We humans have a pronounced 'sweet tooth'. It is a basic taste we favour. When foodstuffs are made more palatable —super-sweet, as in chocolates—they become more desirable. Judy's parents unwittingly played on this instinct until her eating responses were over-stimulated.

Judy was brought up in a household with bad eating habits. Everyone ate excessively. Mother and father propagated the myth that 'it runs in the family' to be over-weight. Whenever she was unhappy, her parents soothed her: "There, there, cheer up. Have a chocolate, or a biscuit." When Judy was naughty or fretful, her parents popped something into her mouth to keep her quiet. Food became an escape from boredom and a release from anxiety. Judy's parents also used food as a reward—an incentive for her to be 'good', or obedient, or quiet.

As a young adult, Judy had weight problems. This made her unhappy, so she ate *more* to relieve her constant concern about weight. She became fatter—and unhappier—and consequently ate more and more. She lived in a vicious circle.

The happy fat lady is a myth.

The apparent bonhomie and cheerfulness is a façade to hide anxiety. She is driven to eat by the need to comfort herself. When Judy went to a party and found that she and Tom were the only over-weight people there, they were instantly linked by the 'fat-is-happy' myth. They began to clown together, emphasising their weight in an unconscious attempt to minimise it.

When Tom and Judy married, they unwittingly encouraged each other's excesses in eating. Judy put on more and more weight. When pregnant, however, Judy had a perfect justification for over-eating. She was *not* over-weight, she was pregnant. All pregnant women have big tummies and gain weight. Unfortunately, after she had the baby, the extra poundage was still with her.

It takes a salutary experience to jolt over-weight people out of their self-delusion. One famous fat lady became stuck in the doorway of a New York restaurant and had to be sawed loose before she sought expert help.

In Judy's case, it was the innocent query by the shop-keeper which made her aware, followed by the incident with the chocolates.

The human mind has its own built-in clocks and meters. Although we do not yet understand how they operate, one cannot deny their existence. Everyone at one time or another will have had the experience of waking in the morning at an exact time without the benefit of an alarm clock. It is possible to use this invisible machinery dramatically in the complex problem of losing weight.

Everyone with a weight problem knows that weight is a subject of baffling complexity. There are multitudes of theories and differing schools of thought, each with its own supporters. Some experts contend that if you eat proteins, which the system burns, and avoid carbohydrates, you must lose weight. Other experts count calories. Another school points out that when you lose weight you slow down your metabolism—the rate at which the body functions, and accordingly, the rate at which it burns up food—so that all diets follow a pattern of diminishing returns. The longer the diet progresses, the slower is the weight loss. The patient burns fewer calories and exists on less food.

I have a radical approach toward the subject of weight loss.

You can lose weight by 'thinking thin'. I have hundreds of case histories which prove that it can be done.

If you can genuinely think you are becoming thin, you can be as successful as a dieter—and often, quite dramatically, more so.

We all know people who eat a lot yet remain slim. They brag: "It doesn't matter what I eat, I don't gain weight."

They are supremely confident in their weight remaining static. They *know* that whatever they over-eat will be burnt away by their fast metabolism. The body's mysterious built-in meters will keep their weight constant.

What of the fat person? He thinks: No matter how little I eat, I put on weight. He has no confidence. His metabolism slows down, and burns up less excess matter. In treating patients who are over-weight, I do not tell them which foods they should eat and which they should avoid. I leave that to the mechanisms within their minds. My advice to a fat person is: Think you are losing weight. Don't make a list of prohibitions. Don't count calories. Don't bother about proteins and carbohydrates. Don't restrict yourself to any particular type of food.

In every orthodox diet, you have to deprive yourself of *something*. And as soon as the diet begins, you become obsessed with the special thing that is denied. This creates a constant strain. There is no need to deprive yourself of anything. But there must be the over-riding consciousness that you are losing weight all the time, that you are not very hungry, that your weight is getting less and less— Think the fat away.

Most important, don't weigh yourself too frequently. Persuade yourself that you will lose one pound in weight per day. Weigh yourself every seven days. The body may regulate its weight erratically, losing no weight one day, and two pounds the following day, but after a week you can easily lose seven pounds.

Some may scoff at this technique. But it works. Here are some case histories:

A patient had gained a stone a year (fourteen lbs) since the age of five. At the age of thirty-five he weighed more

53

than thirty stone (420 lbs). He tried every conceivable diet, but as he lost weight, his metabolism slowed and each diet ground to a halt. We succeeded in 'thinking' his weight down to seventeen stone (238 lbs).

A woman who weighed eighteen and a half stone came to me in desperation. She had been over eighteen stone (259 lbs) for the past twenty years. Diets didn't help her and her health was disintegrating under the enormous extra burden of fat. 'Thinking thin', she lost weight steadily at the rate of one pound per day, for week after week, until she reached eleven stone (154 lbs).

A newspaper columnist asked me to help him lose weight. He said he would report the results of the experiment in his column. He weighed seventeen and a half stone (245 lbs) and wanted to reduce to thirteen and a half stone (185 lbs). I persuaded him to 'think thin', eat anything he liked but in moderation, and he would lose one pound per day until he had reached the desired weight. This journalist's case history is notable because it demonstrated how a human being's clocks, meters and censoring devices can control weight effectively.

The columnist reported that he mischievously ordered a steak and a large helping of chips. He took a mouthful of steak, chewed it, then tried to spear a few chips with his fork. To his astonishment his hand would not obey the command and the fork veered to one side sending the chips flying off the table. A built-in sentinel had signalled: No chips, or it will be impossible to lose a pound every day.

The columnist lost exactly at this rate, measured weekly, until he finally came down to thirteen and a half stone. One year later I checked with the newspaper to find out whether he had remained at his desired weight level. They reported that in the twelve-month period his weight had varied by no more than three pounds. His weight problem was a thing of the past.

Another astounding example of how effective this mental control of weight loss can be, was provided by a woman who consulted me. She proved an excellent patient and lost seventy pounds. One morning she came for her weekly consultation. She was in tears.

"What's the matter?" I asked.

"I'm a complete failure," she cried.

"What do you mean?"

"Well," she said, "everything has been marvellous and I was eating like a bird, but I knew I had to come and see you to be weighed this morning. I don't know what got into me."

"Why, what did you do?"

"I went to the corner shop and bought a pound of butter, a jar of jam and a loaf of bread and I ate it all—the whole lot. I'm so upset. But I couldn't stop myself," she confessed shame-facedly.

We put her on the scale. She had lost exactly seven pounds during the week since she had last seen me. The explanation? Her mind knew she had lost *too much* weight —more than the prescribed pound a day. She felt compelled to stuff herself with food to meet the required reduction of seven pounds. A dramatic example of precision control of weight loss.

Hypnosis *can* be used for weight losing as a means of intensifying the mental attitude of the patient. Under hypnosis, imagination functions at its highest level. But it is possible for the *same* results to be achieved *without* the help of hypnosis.

Follow the example of athletes in establishing the correct mental attitude. A weight-lifter, who is about to hoist an enormous weight will stand for as long as five minutes, studying it. He lifts the weight in his mind, before he does so in substance.

High jumpers do the same. A championship golfer will hit a beautiful shot. Ask him about it, he'll confess that he knew precisely where the ball was going before he made the stroke. The thought was father to the deed. It is confidence which makes the performance possible.

We talk ourselves out of many more things than we talk ourselves into. We can achieve so much more than we ever dream about—if only we learn to utilise the thought mechanisms within ourselves.

Judy Brown was intelligent and quick to learn. We were able to make dramatic improvements. Within months her weight came down to manageable proportions. She will never be thin, but she is no longer gross. Her marriage had been restored. She is happy and the weight loss has been maintained.

3: Girl in Another Town

As John Mackenzie parked his car he wondered what the party would be like. Dull, he decided. It was being held to mark the recent appointment of a young executive from out of town to a more senior position in the insurance firm John worked for. Tonight would serve to introduce the executive and his wife to his new colleagues. The occasion was part of a rigid pattern of social intercourse imposed on members of the firm. Mackenzie had been through it many times before.

He went in and was greeted by familiar faces and familiar voices. The hostess gave him his customary drink without having to ask what it was. He heard office gossip which was old the previous week. He stole a glance at his watch. It was still too early to make his excuses. Perhaps after a few more drinks, and at least a couple of 'informal' speeches by senior members of the firm.

His eyes fell on two new arrivals—young women who appeared to have come to the party unescorted. He knew one girl, Jane. She worked in the claims department. But it was the other woman who drew his attention. She had thick chestnut hair, and her beauty was so distinctive that he noticed the male heads turning throughout the room.

He made his way toward them and greeted Jane who introduced him. "John, meet Alice. Alice is joining us next week. I thought it would be a good idea to bring her tonight so she could meet everyone informally."

John hardly heard the words that followed the girl's name. He held her hand a trifle longer than seemed necessary, but she didn't seem to mind. From that moment, the party couldn't last long enough for John Mackenzie . . .

He appointed himself escort to the girls, fetching drinks for them and steering them from group to group. Without exception he noticed, the men at the party approached

Alice during the evening. But Alice had an aloof quality which deterred them. He admired her more and more. That evening he took her home and was about to kiss her when she quietly turned away. "Good night and thank you," she said, and the door was closed.

When Alice started work with the company she found a bouquet of flowers welcoming her. They were from John.

He courted her assiduously and respectfully. Only after they had been out together several times did she permit him to kiss her. And then it was a chaste kiss. Her aura often stirred him, but Alice would not permit any physical intimacy.

One night they sat up unusually late and Alice confessed her attitude to sex. She regarded sexual activity as valid only within marriage. Now, John Mackenzie knew he would have to marry Alice. It was not that he only wanted her physically. He admired her for her elegance, her dignity, her superb dress sense and her poise. She was a conversationalist, was knowledgeable about current affairs and was a wonderful companion.

Proposing marriage had been on his mind almost from the night they first met. Now he *knew* that he wanted her. And, because he felt such respect for her, he wanted to do things properly. So it had to be marriage.

Mackenzie proposed. Alice accepted, and they celebrated with a dinner party for their close friends and members of John's family. Alice's people lived in another part of the country, and the following weekend Alice took John to meet them. They got on well.

When Alice and John were married three months later, it was a social event. Leading members of the business community attended and the usual speeches were complimentary to both bride and groom. They decided they should spend their honeymoon far from their usual haunts so they drove to a remote village on the coast. It was a long drive but John was exhilarated with anticipation and sexual excitement. His eyes were as often on his bride as they were on the road.

They had rented a cottage overlooking the sea. The

resort had been recommended to John by his closest friend, Andy, who had spent assorted weeks there with assorted girlfriends. Unlike John, Andy didn't take his love life seriously, it was the only point of difference between them.

Now as he surveyed the beautiful coast-line, the white beaches only a few moments' walk from their cottage door, and the air of serenity and remoteness which characterised the setting, John felt grateful to Andy. He thought: if Andy wasn't so oversexed he probably wouldn't have discovered this haven. He chuckled.

He closed the door and took Alice in his arms. They kissed for a long time and she let her head rest on his shoulder. She slipped out of his arms and went into the bathroom. "I must change, darling," she said.

Mackenzie felt himself trembling with happiness. He wanted to dance and shout. He rushed about the cottage and in an instant had the luggage stowed away and his clothes unpacked. He stood in the bedroom not knowing what to expect. For a heady moment he thought Alice might emerge naked. No, he told himself. Alice isn't like that. Then Alice entered. She had changed into a fresh skirt and top.

"Come on, darling," she said, smiling. "Let's go for a long walk. It's so beautiful here, isn't it?"

Hand in hand they walked across springy grass to the sand of the long, open beaches, with the sea rushing almost to their feet, then receding. They walked for several miles, the sea breeze bringing a flush to their cheeks.

"I'm famished," said Alice. "Let's make a great big meal." They returned briskly to the cottage.

When the food was prepared John produced a bottle of Burgundy and they ate, drank and talked, the restless sound of the sea outside, a musical counterpoint to their words.

Eventually, his tongue loosened by the wine, John looked to his bride. "Come on," he said. "Let's go to bed ..." He paused, unsure. Had he been too obvious.

Alice seemed completely in control and John marvelled

59

at her composure. "You go to bed, I'll join you in a moment." She went into the bathroom.

John took off his clothes and slid between the sheets. His pulse was pounding and the heat from his body created a cosy island of comfort under the bedclothes. Alice came into the bedroom. She was in a nightdress which revealed nothing. "Hello, darling," she said, got into bed and switched off the bedside light.

She lay next to him, on her back. John's eyes adjusted to the dim light until he could see her profile next to him. At last, he thought, this woman I've loved for so long is here, in bed, and we are about to share everything.

He reached for her, she turned to him and they kissed. Desire inflamed him, throbbing sensations which filled his being. He kissed her slowly. Alice lay still as he felt her breast, firm beneath his hand. Her nightdress fell away and his leg touched the inside of her thigh. He could not contain himself. As he entered his wife for the first time, the months of waiting propelled him to swift orgasm. Spent, he lowered himself from her body and held her tightly. Love, adoration and satisfaction brought him a feeling of tenderness he had never previously experienced.

"Is that it finished?" she asked. "I must have a shower."

It was as though Alice had thrown iced water over him. It was impossible ... surely she had felt the same as he? The words echoed—'finished ... must have a shower ...'

He heard the sprinkler and Alice's voice, humming a tune. Perhaps she's shy, he thought. That must be it. He rose and put coffee on. He began to feel elated. He had discovered within himself a tremendous sexual potential. The range of his senses while he made love to Alice had astonished him. Physically and mentally, he had soared. He was invincible! He laughed out loud.

John made love to Alice again the next morning but he did not experience the same exhilaration. It was a brief, sweaty encounter and when it was over, Alice quietly moved away from him. She did not speak, simply showered and made the breakfast. They began to plan their day.

That afternoon, Alice had a nap and John went walking

on the deserted beach. He thought of his almost transcendental experience with his wife the night before. It still seemed unbelievable that she had not shared his ecstasy. But Alice was a hyper-sensitive woman and it was possible, he supposed, that in his frenzy he had embarrassed or perhaps overwhelmed her. He had also noticed her lack of enthusiasm during love making that morning. He had read that some people preferred sex at different times to others. Perhaps Alice was not an early morning lover. He decided to confine his romanticism to the hours of darkness.

That evening he announced that he would prepare dinner. She smiled with enjoyment at his thoughtfulness and curled up with a book in an easy chair, while he pottered in the kitchen.

As a bachelor, John had been known among his friends as a fine amateur chef. Tonight he prepared the food with great care. Alice gasped with delight when he presented the meal. John paid particular attention to her glass, hoping that extra wine might help to reduce her shyness when the evening reached its climax in the bedroom.

After the meal, Alice put her arms around his neck and kissed him on the cheek. It was the first affection she had given that day and he responded eagerly.

He kissed her on the mouth and began to touch her breast but she moved away. "Please, John," she said, with a prim gesture. "Not now."

"Why not?"

Alice hesitated. "Well ... if you must ... let's get into bed."

John waited in the bed while Alice busied herself in the bathroom. She came out, wearing her nightdress once again, and put out the light as she pulled the covers over herself. He embraced her and fondled her gently. Tonight he would make sure that he didn't upset her. The bedroom curtains were slightly awry and moonlight fell into the room. He could see Alice's face as she lay immobile in his arms. Her eyes were closed, her face expressionless. She reminded him of an early Madonna painting. With tenderness he began to caress her. Slowly he rose over her and inserted himself. The exquisite sensation brought a gasp of pleasure to his lips. He checked himself. Be considerate, he told himself, and glanced anxiously at Alice.

Her eyelids were screwed together. Her lips and the corners of her mouth were down-turned. Her face expressed with agonising clarity—her disdain and disgust.

John was appalled. He withdrew and lay watching her. "Alice," he said softly.

She opened her eyes. "What's the matter?" she said.

"That's what I want to know," said John.

"I don't know what you mean," said Alice. "Have you ..." she paused. "Have you finished already?"

"No," said John. "I haven't finished."

He saw concern in her eyes. "Isn't that bad for you ... I mean, you'd better finish otherwise you'll feel terrible, won't you?"

John did not know what to say. He decided on discretion. His ardour was gone completely, in any case.

"Don't worry, darling," he said, and kissed her on the forehead. "Let's go to sleep." He turned and lay with his back to her, his mind spinning.

After a little while he felt her hand on his shoulder.

"John" she said, diffidently.

"What is it darling?" he said.

"I just want you to know ..." the words faded into silence.

"What, Alice?"

"Well ... I want you to know that I'll always do my duty as a wife."

So that's it, thought Mackenzie. Duty.

"Don't be upset. There's nothing to worry about," he said mechanically.

Alice soon fell asleep, but John was awake for long hours with his futile thoughts.

For the next few days John did not attempt to make love to Alice. They spent pleasant, lazy times together, talking over every conceivable subject and learning to know each other. They even talked about sex, and strangely enough, it was Alice who brought up the subject.

She told him about a boyfriend she had in college. They went steady for three years, she recalled, and nothing sexual happened between them. Then he begged her to make love. He said he was going out of his mind, even claimed he was doing himself physical harm with sexual frustration.

Eventually, said Alice, against her better judgment, she had agreed, although she felt that sex was the least important element in the relationship between two people.

'He was an animal," said Alice, her nose puckering up in distaste at the memory. "In a way I was glad it happened the way it did because I was able to end the relationship." Alice looked at John intently. "But that's why I wasn't a virgin."

John squeezed her hand. "These things happen," he said. They got into bed, kissed, and Alice was asleep in an instant.

On their last night in the cottage, Alice surprised John by coming to him after the evening meal and kissing him warmly.

"Darling, I want you to make love to me tonight," she said firmly.

"Oh," said John, taken aback.

"I've been thinking," she said, "and I realise I'm not being fair to you. After all you're a strong, healthy man. I can imagine what it does to you, lying in bed with me and not doing anything." She dropped her eyes as though she might blush. "After all," she said, "we are married."

Yes, thought John, we are. And even though Alice might not enjoy the sexual act as much as I do, there's no reason why I shouldn't get as much satisfaction as I can. Especially when she's offering it like this.

In the now familiar ritual he got into bed and lay there, naked. Alice came into the bedroom and put out the light. Tonight, he decided, there would be a slight change. He pulled the covers off the bed so that their bodies were exposed. He glanced at his erection. He looked enormous in the light from the window. He began to slip the nightdress from Alice's body. His nerves were taut, and his hand was quivering. Alice turned her head away slightly, a subtle gesture of aversion. John felt coarse and vulgar. What am I doing, he thought? He felt himself subside like a punctured balloon.

"Come on, dear," said Alice. The first words of sexual encouragement he had heard from her. He felt desperate. I've got to do it. She's expecting it. He looked at his penis and willed it to be erect. But somehow, something he had always taken for granted had acquired a separate identity, a mind of its own.

He took it in his hand in a bid to stimulate it into life. It lay limp, oblivious to his mental commands.

"What's the matter, darling?" said Alice. She saw him fingering himself and he felt ashamed. "I don't feel like sex, Alice. I think I've got some sort of inflammation," he lied impulsively. Anything to save the embarrassment. Did she think I was masturbating, he thought miserably.

"You better have it seen to, dear," said Alice, the concerned young wife. She kissed him on the cheek. "You're sure you don't want to ...?"

"I'm sure, darling," he said quickly.

They turned, worlds apart in the same bed, and finally found the solace of sleep.

To their friends, the marriage of John Mackenzie and Alice was a success. They were a handsome couple and were welcome at all the social occasions.

John's father showed his approval by acquiring a junior partnership for him in a firm of insurance brokers. Financially, John was secure. Professionally, he enjoyed his work and was good at it. But his marriage was not what he had hoped it would be.

Realising that he needed a second opinion, John took his problem to Andy, his best friend. They discussed the matter in Andy's apartment—a bachelor pad designed and furnished for seduction. Andy's life-style had always been far removed from John's. Mackenzie was a hard-worker, who expended his energies in clearly defined patterns. He was a romantic and inclined to put women on pedestals. Now that his idealistic marriage dream was unfulfilled, he turned to Andy for counsel.

"I can't understand it," he said. Andy, wearing a dramatic white sweater, grinned.

Mackenzie anticipated his friend's comment. 'Okay ... I know you're a cynic about women. You happen to be a natural dilettante ... with women and with work."

Andy smiled superciliously. "Well, if your father had been thoughtful enough to leave you a guaranteed income, you probably would be too."

"No doubt," said John. "But let's talk about me, not you." He helped himself to another beer. "I can't really complain about Alice. In most respects she's great. But somehow I feel we should be having a stupendous sex life ..."

Even though Andy was a lifelong friend, John felt embarrassed, and he paused to choose his words.

"Don't tell me she's frigid!" said Andy. "A beauty like that ... mind you it does happen. You can never tell what you're getting until it's too late."

Mackenzie did not reply. He drank his beer and put the empty glass down. Andy knew his friend and he looked at him, searchingly.

"Come on," he commanded. "Out with it. Something's upsetting you and now you're beating around the bush. Is she messing around with other men?"

John grinned ruefully. "Trust you to think on those lines. No, it's nothing like that. Alice is trustworthy." He shook his head and lapsed into silence again.

Andy thrust another beer towards him. "Drink up. Maybe booze will loosen your tongue. It's me, Andy, remember?"

John sipped at his drink. 'It's not Alice," he said. "It's me."

"What?" Andy was astounded. "Don't tell me you've developed a wandering eye?" He laughed facetiously.

Mackenzie felt a spurt of anger. "Don't be so damned

65

stupid," he said acidly. "What I'm trying to tell you . . . I can't get it up any more. In other words, I'm impotent."

Andy was horrified. "Impotent!" he said. He looked at John, his mouth agape. "But you're only twenty-six!"

"Twenty-seven," said Mackenzie.

"What's the difference. You're young! Impotence only happens to old codgers!" Andy was disturbed, the practised seducer haunted by the spectre of a missing sex life.

"It happened on our honeymoon," said John miserably. "Since then I occasionally manage to make love, but most of the time the damned thing just droops."

In his agitation, Mackenzie strode about the apartment, slamming his clenched fist into his hand.

"What I can't understand is that the first time we made it together it was fantastic. I've never had a sensation like it in my life. But then I discovered it was one-sided. Alice doesn't enjoy sex on the same level as me, but she's always willing and she only has to come near me to turn me on. Yet, no matter how much I try, I can't perform."

Mackenzie sat with a groan. "The awful thing is that Alice seems to think I've gone off her. Even though she doesn't really enjoy sex, she thinks if I don't make love to her once a week, I'm annoyed and I don't love her. You know what women are!"

"I've never had that sort of trouble, thank heavens," said Andy fervently. "So I can't advise you by personal experience. Maybe you should see a psychiatrist."

Mackenzie snorted. "My trouble's not in my head, dammit, it's somewhere else!"

"Tell me," said Andy morbidly fascinated by his friend's ailment, "can't you get an erection at all? I mean, don't you wake up hard in the morning, like everyone else?"

"That's another strange thing," said John. "I do. But it doesn't last. It just sort of . . . evaporates. You know, the urge and the ability."

"You've certainly got problems," said Andy. "Why don't you go for a check-up. You never know, it might be something else that's causing the trouble."

"I suppose you're right," said John.

The friends sat and discussed the problem. As Mackenzie unburdened himself, Andy watched him with narrowed eyes. An idea was forming. While John fetched another beer, he went to his bedroom and returned with a book. He slid it unobtrusively onto the bar top.

"How'd you like a sandwich?" he asked John.

"Great idea," said Mackenzie. Andy left him alone at the bar and went into the kitchen. He did not return for five minutes.

Mackenzie was immersed in the book, turning the pages slowly. His drink stood next to him forgotten.

"Has it turned you on yet?" Andy asked suddenly.

John started with surprise. "What?" he said blankly. He looked down. "Good Lord," he said with surprise. "It's happened."

"I thought so," said Andy, with satisfaction. "That's real Swedish pornography. Guaranteed to turn anyone on. And you're no exception.

"I diagnose that you're not impotent at all, except with Alice. You've got some sort of mental block."

John Mackenzie put down the book with a grunt. "Look, that's rubbish. Just because I get excited looking at this sort of thing doesn't mean I'd be able to perform if there was a woman in the room with me. That's a different proposition."

"I'm not so sure," said Andy, eyeing his distraught friend.

John ate his sandwich then decided it was time to go.

"I'll give you a ring next week," said Andy, as he saw John to the door. He returned to the bar and sat, deep in thought. The solution to John's problem came to him in a few moments. I'll introduce him to Marilyn, he thought.

Marilyn lived in a neighbouring city and Andy usually looked her up when he was in that area. He remembered that John had said he would be visiting that city on business next week. Ideal! thought Andy, pleased with his resourcefulness. I'll go along with him, then I'll set up something for the evening. He picked up the phone and dialled Marilyn's number. She was in, and it took only moments to explain the situation.

"See you on Thursday," he said, "And you know what to do. Treat him with kid gloves." He hung up, smiling.

From his window seat it seemed to John that the jet was swivelling on its wing-tip as it banked sharply after take-off. The urban sprawl spiralled past his area of vision and the plane settled on course.

Andy loosened his seat belt. "Come on! Don't look so damned miserable! This is going to be the most enjoyable business trip you've ever been on . . ."

He pressed the button for service and looked at his watch. "We've got a comfortable hour and a half to do some drinking. Then we'll be met at the airport and tonight we're going to have the time of our lives."

John looked at his friend, immaculate as usual, radiating irresponsibility. He could readily understand why women went for Andy. He was a naughty child with sexual overtones. But John was a little uneasy about Andy's enthusiasm.

"What do you mean . . . the time of our lives?" he asked.

"Just what I say. A good time. No hang-ups. No worries to interfere with enjoyment."

"Be more specific," said John, grinning in spite of himself.

"We're going to have dinner with some friends of mine and then to a club." He lifted a hand . . . "Don't worry, I know you have a business appointment in the morning. We'll have you in bed by one a.m. How's that?"

"Fine," said John. The stewardess arrived and they ordered drinks. John settled himself. He had to admit that Andy's enthusiasm was infectious. He felt like a schoolboy playing truant. Originally, when he realised that this trip was necessary, he had planned to stay for only one night. According to his original schedule he would have flown back the following afternoon, but Andy had persuaded him to stay an extra day.

"A day off will do you the world of good," Andy had said. "Particularly when I'll be there to show you the sights . . ."

Now it was Wednesday afternoon. He was booked on a late afternoon return flight on Friday. Alice would meet him at the airport. The thought of Alice made him tense, and he moved irritably in his seat. After his talk with Andy he had seen a doctor (Andy's, of course) and had been pronounced fit and well. "Many men have temporary impotence," the medical man had said assuringly. Business worries, family responsibilities, and so forth. I'm sure it's only temporary. Organically, there is nothing wrong with you. You should be capable of a vigorous sex life."

He'd left the consulting room feeling considerably more confident than before, but the feeling was short-lived. His next encounter with Alice was as abortive as his previous endeavours.

"Friday night," thought John. "We've fallen into a routine like a couple married for thirty years." He recalled his relief when Alice told him that she preferred a regular schedule for sex. Friday was the night. Alice would acquit herself of her obligations every Friday night ... and he would be spared the frustration of attempting to function sexually on the other six nights.

A situation had developed in which he could never be sure whether he would be *able* to make love to Alice. They would go through the preliminaries, sometimes even dining by candlelight, as though obeying the advice in a manual to honeymooners on how to conquer first night nerves.

Sometimes Alice would kiss and cuddle him and he would have a resurgence of his sexual urge. But, by the time Alice had gone to the bathroom, changed, re-emerged, and entered the bed, his sex drive had always vanished, beyond recall. Alice, submissive and expectant, would lie in bed waiting for him to assert his masculinity and make love to her. He would suffer silent torment, defeated by his recalcitrant member.

At first he resorted to excuses, lies about feigned indispositions, to hide his indescribable embarrassment. Then, one night he short-circuited the sorry situation by saying he had a business commitment and would not be home until late.

"Don't wait up for me, darling," he'd said. "I'll be exhausted when I get in. Don't forget, I was up early this morning!"

Alice gave him the look of a woman undeceived by male guile. Then, to his astonishment, came floods of tears. He was dumbfounded. This was the last thing he had expected. He held Alice and cupped her face in his hands. The tears rolling down her cheeks seemed to emphasise her beauty, imbuing her with a vulnerability which was normally not visible.

"You don't love me!" she cried. "You're not interested in making love to me, you've always an excuse. There's another woman, admit it ..." She collapsed in another torrent of tears.

Agitated and upset, John kissed and consoled her, repeated over and over that he loved no one else, could love no one else, and had never looked at another woman. Gradually she regained her composure. John picked her up bodily, carried her into the bedroom, and made love to her. Miraculously, he was restored. After he had spent himself he turned to her, smiling: "There! You see!"

But Alice was already slipping out of bed, clutching her clothes, heading for the bathroom. John felt cheated, as though denied something which was his due. After all, he'd made love, hadn't he?

Anyway, there had not been a recurrence of the tears, and he was grateful for that. But for the last couple of weeks those Friday night sessions had assumed an importance to him out of all proportion.

Normally he and Alice had fine verbal communication. Conversationally they could talk indefinitely and neither of them had ever been at a loss for words. Yet, last Friday night, he had felt unaccountably ill at ease, had fidgeted in his chair and silence had fallen between them repeatedly.

He was disturbed out of his reverie by Andy, shaking him. "Come on," he said, "I've ordered you another drink and you haven't even finished the first one."

John Mackenzie downed the drink and decided Andy was right. He did need a couple of days' relaxation. He

70

tried to think himself into a holiday mood. For two days, apart from tomorrow morning, he would be meeting new faces in new surroundings. He could do what he liked. The prospect was pleasing. He leaned back in his seat and stretched his legs.

"Cheers," he said, raising his glass.

"That's better!" said Andy.

As they walked into the airport building John Mackenzie looked about him. Not one familiar face. It gave him a strange irresponsible feeling. He saw a trim blonde with a flashing smile, waving. He was momentarily taken aback when he realised the blonde must be waving at them. He grinned self-consciously and looked at Andy.

His friend was waving back, his eye twinkling with obvious delight.

The blonde dived into Andy's arms. They kissed, taking their time, while John stood alongside, feeling an outsider.

When they eventually untangled themselves, Andy introduced the 'bombshell'. "John—Amy," she smiled, shook his hand and returned all her attention to Andy. John, now familiar with this, moved off to collect the luggage.

Amy drove them into town. She was an outgoing girl and by the time they pulled up at the hotel, John knew that she was a dancer, that she was rehearsing for a new show, and that she was quite deranged about Andy.

"We'll be back for you in an hour," said Andy. "Shower, change your shirt, have a drink, then we'll be off for a night to remember." Amy gunned the car and John stood there grinning, as they shot into the stream of traffic.

He booked into the hotel and when he was in his room, felt the adrenalin of anticipation in his veins. "I'm a bachelor again," he thought flippantly. He toasted himself in the bathroom mirror.

John's phone rang. It was the reception desk, advising him that Andy was waiting in the foyer. He went down, whistling. He and Andy climbed into Amy's car and drove into the bustle of the city. Andy and Amy were in a giggly mood. They had the slightly glazed look of a couple who had just made love. Once again he felt the odd man out. As though sensing his mood, Andy seized him by the arm. "Don't think you're going to be the gooseberry tonight!" he said.

"What do you mean?" said John.

"Amy has a friend, name of Marilyn. It so happens that her date has let her down. I've nominated you as substitute."

"Come on," said John. "Don't say you've fixed me a blind date?" He looked pained.

"Marilyn's a great girl," said Amy. "The only reason she's going out with you is because you're a friend of Andy's, and I persuaded her that any friend of Andy's must be all right."

Andy said: "We're going to this Italian restaurant. Small place, home-made grub ... lots of atmosphere. We'll have a chance to talk."

"All right," said John. He watched the traffic through the car window. I've nothing to lose, he thought. I just hope tonight will be different.

Expertly, Amy nudged the car into a parking area. "Come on," she said. "We're having a drink with Marilyn first."

It was a stylish building. Marilyn's apartment was on the fourteenth floor. Andy and Amy bundled through the door and John heard excited sounds of greeting. Then Amy took him by the hand. "John," she said, "I want you to meet Marilyn," and she giggled like a conspirator.

John took Marilyn's hand and said hello. She was about five foot seven with dark colouring. He was disappointed that she was not really pretty. Her eyes were too small, her lips too pronounced. A slightly coarse face and not particularly animated. He clothing was quiet.

"Andy's spoken about you," said Marilyn. "It's nice to meet you." They drifted to the cocktail bar in a corner of the dimly lit lounge. The apartment had an air of relaxed opulence. John felt, astonishingly, at ease. It was as though Marilyn's plainness had removed a threat.

They sat at the bar and Marilyn poured drinks. She asked them, individually, whether they wanted coffee, fruit juice or alcohol. John thought this considerate as he was not a regular drinker. He could hold liquor, but he associated alcohol with special occasions.

"I'll have a Scotch on the rocks," he said, in reply to Marilyn's enquiry. He wanted tonight to be special!

After a while Andy suggested they go to dinner. The restaurant was a family one, run by a husband and wife and typical of such establishments anywhere in the world. In one corner sat friends of the family, erupting in laughter and excited conversation as they dug into spaghetti and ravioli. Pitchers of wine dotted the tables.

As the four of them drank and talked, their personalities fell into place. Andy was the star, cracking jokes and steering the conversation. His girl friend, Amy, was vivacity itself, her smile a delight. John, too, made humorous contributions and was able to keep the conversation going without undue effort.

At first, blinded by Amy's looks, John hardly noticed Marilyn. But, gradually, he became conscious of her. She seemed to anticipate his requirements—an attitude which was quite new to him. She impinged on his awareness in small things—passing the salt, arranging bowls of food so that they were easily to hand, listening attentively when he spoke. As the evening progressed he felt her hand on his arm, warmly intimate. She would squeeze it in appreciation of a witticism or nudge him with delight when they laughed together.

After dinner they moved to a jazz club where a Dixieland band pounded out a simple yet infectious beat.

They danced and John was instantly surprised. Marilyn moved against him as though they were one person. He felt her hand stroking his neck. He was so unused to such open affection that he pulled away briefly with a startled movement. At once he apologised, and held her close again. Marilyn said nothing but gave a smile and continued stroking his neck—she began to nibble his ear.

As they shuffled around the floor to the simple rhythm,

73

Marilyn shifted subtly until her groin was pressed to his.

She pulled away slightly and looked up at him directly. Her dark brown eyes had a permanently warm, slightly amused expression.

"You're very affectionate, you know," she said. Her voice was in the lower feminine register.

John laughed, a little embarrassed. "It's you," he said, "it's easy to be affectionate towards someone as ..." he groped for the right word ... "warm as you."

"I mean it," said Marilyn. "You're gentle. I like gentle people."

She came close to him again and as he became aware of the complete femininity of her, of the voluptuousness beneath the conservative attire, of her sheer physical attractiveness, he experienced the stirrings of desire. To his relief the band stopped and they went to their table, hand in hand.

The girls retired to the powder-room and Andy leaned across to John.

"You seem to be enjoying yourself?" He grinned.

"You're right," said John. "I haven't been so relaxed for years. That's quite a beauty you have."

"Amy's a knock-out," agreed Andy. "But what about Marilyn? She's great company, isn't she?"

"A nice girl," said John. "And affectionate. Just what I need." A thought struck him. "What does she do? I don't think she's said a word about herself so far. She seems to do all the listening."

"Oh," said Andy. "Oh, yes, she has some sort of job in a publishing house. But I think she used to be married to a rich old guy and she gets a fat alimony cheque every month."

Marilyn took him back to the dance floor as soon as the music resumed. They spent long moments moving quietly in each other's arms. There was no need for conversation. John was almost annoyed when Andy reminded him of the time. "It's 12.30," he said. "You told me to remind you. That early appointment ..."

"Yes, I know," said John.

"Why don't you let Marilyn run you back to the hotel?" said Andy. "Amy's got some friends from a show coming here later so we'll have to wait for them. I'll phone you tomorrow.'

John and Marilyn left them, chatting cheerily to each other.

"We've got time for a night-cap?" asked Marilyn softly, as she put the car into gear.

"Well, yes," said John, "but I don't want to put you to any trouble."

"It's no trouble," said Marilyn. "Anyway my place is only five minutes' drive from your hotel. I'll run you home afterwards."

"What time do you go to work tomorrow?" asked John. "I've got to be up bright and early."

"I work as a part-time reader for a publishing house," said Marilyn. "And I work at home. So I can plan my day as I like."

"That's a nice arrangement," said John.

"Yes," she said, glanced sideways at him, and smiled.

She has a very sensual face, thought John. For some reason his wife suddenly flashed into his thoughts. He realised, with a jolt, that it was the first time he'd thought of Alice all night. He felt unaccountably guilty.

Marilyn parked the car and they went into her apartment block. In the brighter light of the foyer John noticed that her grooming was immaculate. Her finger-nails were polished and manicured, her make-up still perfect. Once in her apartment she insisted on taking off his jacket and tie and hanging them up. She fixed him a drink and turned down the lights so that they sat together, in a glow of understated, direct lighting. John felt his tension finally dissolve.

He began to talk openly to Marilyn, prompted by her questions. When words faltered she prodded him verbally into divulging more about himself. Nudged on by her interest, he spoke of his early years with his parents, his time in college—he even found himself talking about his business life. He thought, surely nothing bored a woman

75

as much as a man's account of his office problems. But as he looked at Marilyn for any signs of restlessness, he found none. "Go on," she said, and reminded him of where his conversation had tailed off ...

Reassured, he spoke with freedom. He even told her about his wife and how there had been no doubt in his mind that he would eventually marry Alice. Suddenly discretion asserted itself. He would say no more about his marriage. After all, this girl was a stranger, even though she was charming and sympathetic.

"Have you ever been married?" he asked Marilyn.

"Yes," she said. "Twice. The first time I was too young."

"And the second time?"

"He was too old." She laughed. "And too rich. But we're still friends. I see him regularly."

She replenished his glass and came to his side. "I might have put too much Scotch in it," she said. "Try it first."

He sipped it. "No. It's fine."

Her hand was still on his. He put down his glass and she moved closer to him. His lips, still chilled from the iced drink, felt her warm, generous mouth. She seemed to enfold him. They kissed for a long time. While it lasted, John Mackenzie had no conscious thoughts. He was suspended in physical sensation.

Slowly, Marilyn broke the embrace. She rested her head on his shoulder. What am I doing? he thought. Alice's face loomed before him. I should go, he told himself. He felt Marilyn kissing him again, lightly, coquettishly.

He felt her thigh against his. As they turned in gentle affectionate movements, her leg massaged his groin. In an instant he had an enormous throbbing erection. I must go! a voice cried, but it was overwhelmed by sensual awareness.

"Come, darling," said Marilyn. She kissed him quickly and then, to his astonishment, licked his cheek. The single gesture was more erotic than he could ever have imagined.

She moved him across the deeply carpeted lounge, kissing him, caressing him, whispering 'darling' and 'lover' in his ear.

I'm being seduced, he thought helplessly. It's the first

time it's ever happened to me . . . . And I'm enjoying it!

She led him into the bedroom, dominated by a huge bed. A mirror ran along one wall. The lights were low, but not too dark to limit vision. Marilyn closed the bedroom door behind them. A final gesture, as though John's line of retreat had been cut.

"Lie down," said Marilyn, and gave him a friendly push in the chest. He fell backwards on to the bed and laughed. Triggered by nervousness, the laugh grew until he was helpless, shaking with amusement. Marilyn caught his mood and also laughed. John rolled about on the expanse of bed and wriggled out of his shirt. It was the biggest bed he'd ever seen. Even when he stretched his arms he barely encompassed the breadth of it.

He flicked his shoes off and they fell silently on to the deep carpet. Marilyn had disappeared. He felt chilled. She was in the bathroom. She would come out and it would be Alice in that hideous nightgown. The fantasy evaporated as Marilyn emerged. She had changed. She wore only diaphanous underwear. She was tanned the colour of dark chocolate. Her hair was down, resting on her shoulders. She had slightly chubby knees which gave her the look of a nymphet schoolgirl.

She was smiling a languorous smile. She rolled on to the bed and kept rolling. She made two full revolutions before she reached him and the absurdity of the action made him laugh again. She was next to him now, freshly perfumed. The musky aroma caught his throat. She buried her face in his neck and her arms circled his back. She ran her long nails lightly over his skin causing him to twitch involuntarily. He lifted her face and kissed her. Her breath was sweet. He felt her other hand wander down his chest, along his belly, her fingers tangling gently in the hairs above his groin. She traced patterns on him with her fingers. She giggled in his ear, and he kissed her again. Her lips were moist and he could taste sexual excitement. Marilyn's hand moved lower and he felt her fingers on his testicles. She squeezed them gently, rhythmically, then lightly tickled the surrounding area. Shudders of pleasure coursed through

77

John Mackenzie's body. A moan escaped from his lips. Her hand still active, Marilyn stopped kissing his mouth and moved her lips to his neck, then down his chest, lingering around his navel and tickling it with her tongue.

God, thought Mackenzie. I don't believe it. He could actually feel physical delight coursing up and down his body, as thought he were in a sensual fever.

Marilyn took the head of his penis in her mouth and sucked it. At once John was caught in a convulsive climax which left him gasping. Slowly he came back to more placid appreciation. "I'm sorry," he murmured. "I couldn't hold back any longer."

"That's the name of the game," said Marilyn, her voice husky. "Don't apologise, darling. It's my turn next!" She rolled off the bed. "Don't move," she commanded, and went into the bathroom, returning with a hand-towel. "I'll bring you a drink." She ran on tiptoes out of the bedroom. He saw the flash of untanned skin, stark against her deep tan. It looked as though she was wearing a white bikini.

She came back with two glasses. She had made cocktails. He was amazed. He had never been so fussed over, pampered, spoiled and sexually pleased.

He took the drink and kissed her lightly on the mouth. In one brief evening, this girl had created a sense of intimacy and openness which he had never been able to associate with sex before. "You make me feel like a Sultan," he said.

She smiled. "Well, you're certainly not a eunuch!" She gave an amused glance downward. He was rampant again. He thought: And yesterday I was impotent. Marilyn was watching him with a curiously knowing smile.

"I liked you from the moment we met," she said suddenly. "I'm an impulsive person. Then when I discovered how gentle you were ..." She didn't finish the sentence but gave him a lingering gaze.

"I don't know if you're aware of it," she said, "but tenderness is extremely rare among men. Passion and lust there's plenty of, but tenderness is a rara avis."

"But that's what it's about," said John. "Isn't it?"

"Of course, lover," said Marilyn, and seized him again. This time John Mackenzie adopted the dominant role in their love-making and used all his sensitivity to please his bed companion. Her gradually mounting cries and groans proved that he succeeded.

They made love repeatedly during the night. Mackenzie would doze, only to be awakened by Marilyn to a new, luxurious awareness of sex.

In the morning, she shook him gently. "It's time," she said. "You have an early appointment."

He glanced at his watch. There was a fresh cup of coffee at the bedside. Marilyn wore a light blue negligee, her hair was freshly brushed and her face glowed with cleanliness. He noticed a suggestion of newly applied eye make-up.

He swung his legs off the bed so he could drink his coffee in greater comfort. Somehow he became entangled with Marilyn. Suddenly they were together and once again her skill brought him to a shuddering ecstatic climax.

"I'll be home all day, working," said Marilyn as she saw him to the door. "I hope you'll come back . . ."

John rolled his eyes. "You must be joking. I'll see you before lunch."

Although he had only the minimum of sleep, John Mackenzie felt sharply attuned, alert and full of confidence. When he met Andy later that day Andy commented on his bright spirits. John smiled. "I pulled off a good deal," he said. "Better than I'd hoped."

"I'm glad to hear it. Now that dreary business is out of the way, we can carry on with the revels!"

"You bet!" said John.

John Mackenzie stayed with Marilyn that night and they spent the following day together. She declined his invitation to the airport. "I don't like farewells," she said. "Just keep in touch. You've got my phone number. Next time you're in town we'll see each other again."

He was on the point of blurting out an emotional protestation but her face deterred him.

"Go on!" she said, in the tone of mock-command which he'd come to recognise as typical of her. "If you're going, go!" She shooed him out of the apartment.

On the plane, John Mackenzie felt the euphoria drain out of him. Andy snoozed, next to him exhausted by his roistering two days.

Alice, thought John. What about Alice? We'll meet at the airport. He looked at himself nervously, as though he might see some visible sign of betrayal which he could hide before Alice's eye fell upon it.

I've been unfaithful to my wife for the first time. Even as he thought it, he knew it would not be the last time. He brushed his hand over his eyes. Anxiety began to knot within him. For two days he had known enjoyment, had been fully alive. Now, as the jet whisked him back to home, wife, job and responsibilities, he seemed to be shedding his happiness and replacing it with anxiety.

Rubbish, he thought. Be positive. He knew, now, that his impotence was only related to Alice. Or, more specifically his impotence was certainly not apparent with Marilyn. Erotic memories flooded his mind. No, he need never worry about that again. He remembered the first night of his honeymoon. He had suspected then that he had great potential for sex and this had been proved by his encounter with Marilyn. What a fantastic woman, he thought with burgeoning affection. The most loving, thoughtful and attentive person he had ever met.

Andy shifted in his seat and slowly awakened, disturbed by the announcement through the loudspeaker that the plane was about to land. He straightened and rubbed his eyes, refreshed. He felt fine. It had been a successful outing in every respect. He glanced at John, relaxing in his seat with a half-smile on his lips.

"How're you feeling?" he asked.

John looked up startled out of his reverie. "Fine. Just fine."

"Penny for your thoughts," said Andy knowing exactly what his friend was thinking.

"Oh," John replied looking flustered. "I was just thinking how much I enjoyed myself." He looked at Andy. "Thanks. I didn't realise how much I needed a break."

"And Marilyn? Did you find her pleasing?"

"What do you mean?" said John sharply.

Andy looked knowingly at his naive friend.

"How did you find her in bed? She's something else, isn't she?"

"How do you know?" said John his eyes flashing.

Oh my God, he's jealous, Andy realised.

"You haven't fallen for sweet little Marilyn, have you?" he asked.

"Not at all," replied John too brusquely. "But what did you mean by that crack? I thought you hadn't met her before!"

"I didn't say that. If you think back, you'll remember I told you that Marilyn was a friend of Amy's and she needed a date. But I've known Marilyn a long time."

Andy could see the tightness of suppressed anger around John's mouth. He knew, intuitively, that John had experienced a sexual encounter which was, if anything, *too* successful. The plane was making its final approach. Andy decided the time had come to tell the truth. He couldn't permit John to rush headlong into a fool's paradise.

"Look, John" he said, and put his hand on John's arm, "I wanted to know if Marilyn pleased you. I have a proprietorial right to know . . ." He let the phrase tail off.

John looked genuinely puzzled. "I don't understand you. Stop talking in riddles."

"I mean that it cost me plenty to have Marilyn entertain you and I wanted to know if she did her duty."

John's face went ashen as the blood drained from it.

"Now don't go off the deep end," said Andy. He spoke swiftly to ward off John's anger. "I wanted to do you a favour. All that nonsense about you being impotent—I wanted you to find out that you're as good as any man. What better way to do that than to make use of someone I knew personally to be an expert. A sexpert, if you like." He ventured a small laugh at his desperate witticism.

John was glaring at him.

"So she's a whore. Just a whore . . ."

Andy realised that he had misconstrued his friend's reaction. He had thought John was furious because he'd been fobbed off with a whore. But John was upset *because* the girl was a whore. His idiot of a friend had fallen head over heels for the first woman who had given him a good tumble.

"Whore is an unsophisticated word," said Andy. The plane swooped down and its wheels trundled along the tarmac. "It implies vulgarity and cheapness. You can't say that Marilyn is vulgar or cheap. She's an exclusive lady with a select clientele. She doesn't accept anyone, you know. She enjoys sex and likes a variety of lovers so she only entertains men she would go to bed with anyway. She also makes a lot of money. The job with the publisher is real, but it's no more than a hobby. The senior editor is one of her clients. Let's call Marilyn a lady of pleasure and leisure." Andy leaned forward. "But more important than Marilyn is *your* state of mind. Did you make it with her?"

"Yes," said John shortly. "Very definitely and very wonderfully."

"I'm glad. Don't say old Andy doesn't take care of you. And remember, she's there whenever you want her." Andy stretched luxuriously. "It's Friday night. We've only been away since Wednesday but it seems as though we've been in another world."

Friday night, thought John Mackenzie, and anxiety impaled him. Duty night in the Mackenzie household. Alice is in the terminal, waiting for me. He rested his head on his hand and looked into the dark as the plane came to a halt.

As they walked through the concourse John felt Andy dig his ribs. "Look," said Andy. Seated on a bench, knees crossed, reading a magazine was Alice. John had a sense of shock at her beauty. "Wow," said Andy. "Look around her." John saw a knot of men sitting nearby, ogling Alice openly. Andy pulled him to a halt and for a few seconds they watched. Men everywhere were watching Alice, some openly, some discreetly, but Alice was unaware of their attention.

"I know," said John. "It drives me mad but what can you do about it?"

They walked to his wife and as she saw them she rose smiling, shaking her chestnut hair from her face. She offered her cheek for a perfunctory kiss to them both.

"Your plane was on time," she said cheerfully.

Andy was watching her with his customary amused expression. "Alice, there's something I've always wanted to know."

"What's that?" she asked.

"A beautiful girl like you, surrounded by all these lecherous men—" he gestured, and Alice seemed to see the male faces for the first time—"what effect does it have on you? Do you find it flattering, repulsive, or what?"

Alice thought for a while unsmilingly. "Well," she said, "I don't feel anything. They're just men. What can you expect from them? Let's collect your luggage." She turned on her heel and the conversation was closed.

At first John thought his unfaithfulness would loom between them. But after the first few minutes of being reunited with his wife he realised this was ridiculous. To Alice, nothing had changed. What you don't know doesn't hurt you, he thought. He had never subscribed to that cynical view of marriage up till then.

As they drove home, Alice asked how the trip had been. Fine, he said. He'd organised the deal without trouble. Had he met anyone he knew? No, he said. He paused, undecided whether to embellish or not. He decided to stick to the truth if possible. He said Andy had introduced him to some friends and they had gone to dinner. Alice said someone from out of town had phoned and left a number. What was his name again? Oh yes, Oliver. A Mr Oliver. That's right, he'd said. He was a recent client of the firm.

Back in the trivia of domestic familiarity, John Mackenzie felt an odd mixture of contentment and irritation. Where was the intoxicating newness that he had known

83

during the past two days? Yet, as he looked at his beautifully groomed wife, he knew that he loved her. It was the love that came with familiarity, and it grew in spite of arguments, irritations and irascibility. The sort of love that produced a telepathic understanding between two people. If only . . . Tonight was Friday night. He wondered how it would be coming to Alice, after his sexual adventures with someone else. He drove, silently, as Alice chatted.

At home they ate, talked and watched television. John discovered that he was looking forward to bedtime. Perhaps the refresher course in sex was just what he'd needed. Perhaps he could now inspire Alice to enjoyment. He saw the prospect as a challenge. With his new experience, perhaps he could coax his wife into shared ecstasies. But to do this, they would have to depart from the dull routine in which they had settled.

When Alice made her inevitable departure into the bathroom, John did not get into bed. Wearing only his briefs, he sat waiting for her.

When Alice came into the bedroom in her customary nightgown, he stood up and embraced her.

"Darling," he said. "We're almost an old married couple aren't we?"

She smiled softly. "I suppose so."

"Well, I've got a suggestion. When we make love . . ." he paused. Alice's lips tightened, imperceptibly.

"Yes . . ." she said.

"Well," John was beginning to flounder. Why could he be so honest and free with Marilyn and yet with his own wife he was a tongue-tied idiot? He had started with the intention of saying something important, and nothing was going to stop him from completing the statement.

"Well, I think we've fallen into a routine, when we make love. There's nothing more boring than routine"—he hastened an amendment—"I'm not suggesting that making love to you is boring, it's just that, you know, variety is the spice of life." He tailed off. Alice was looking at him intently.

"Exactly what do you have in mind," she said very quietly.

"Nothing dramatic, darling," he said. "I was going to suggest that we take our clothes off before we get into bed. After all you have a fabulous figure and, you know, there can be lots of visual erotic sensations . . ."

Alice stood, her eyes glittering. "You mean you want me to flaunt my body like a stripper." Her voice rose, with a suggestion of hysteria. "What do you think I am? A common whore?"

John Mackenzie felt himself flush. If Alice had struck him she could not have affected him more. Alice was shrieking shrilly. "My mother warned me! All men are animals, she said, and sex is filthy. She was right. You have been placed on this earth as a woman, she told me, and you must fulfil your wifely duties." The words were a sonorous cadence, the recitation of a well worn religious litany.

"The only blessing from sex is children. That's what she told me." Alice collapsed on the bed, sobbing. "If I could only get pregnant I could stop these horrible Friday nights." She lay on the bed, knees drawn up, whimpering.

John, aghast, looked at his crumpled, defeated wife. Her façade of impregnable beauty and composure was shattered. Gently he stroked her forehead and kissed away her tears. She fell asleep in his arms, like a child.

Three months later, Andy Thompson sat in his apartment. He looked at his watch. John Mackenzie was ten minutes late. I hope he comes, thought Andy. He's *got* to come. He pondered over his plan. For many weeks Andy had been conscious of his responsibility to a friend visibly destroying himself. John was coming apart, and Andy watched, not knowing what to do about it. To make matters worse, Mackenzie, who had always brought his problems to Andy, now avoided him. That's why he *must* come tonight. He's got to listen to me. The bell rang. He's arrived, thought Andy. He let John in, put him at the bar, took his coat, and poured him a drink.

"Long time no see," he said. It had been nearly two months since they had spoken. John looked drawn, slight smudges under his eyes. The signs of stress.

"Yes," said John. "I've been away a lot."

"I know," said Andy. "Anyway, good health," he raised his glass.

They talked superficially whilst Andy kept replenishing John's glass. John always needed encouragement before he could discuss personal matters.

"How's business?" asked Andy lightly. He had decided, earlier, that this was the best way to dig out John's personal problems.

"Not too good," said John, listlessly.

"Frankly, I've heard some disturbing stories," said Andy.

"For instance?" John didn't seem particularly perturbed.

"There's a story that you're neglecting your responsibilities."

"Really?" John shrugged.

"And I know Alice isn't happy."

"That I can understand," said John sourly. "But how did you hear it?"

"She phoned me," said Andy. "She's worried about your marriage."

"All right," said John wearily. He gave Andy his full attention. "I know you didn't invite me here for nothing. Tell me everything you've heard about the disintegration of John Mackenzie ... and his marriage."

"It's a sad story. Are you sure you want to hear it?"

"Proceed," said John, with mock pomposity.

"My information," said Andy, matching his friend's mood, "is that John Mackenzie developed a sexual block with his wife, was encouraged to have an affair with a professional lady, discovered that he wasn't impotent, and has since become infatuated with the said professional lady, to the detriment of his business and his marriage."

Andy paused, dramatically, then abandoned the theatrics. He spoke to John normally. "You've been spending more time with Marilyn than you have with Alice. Admit it!"

"Yes," said John.

"You must be spending money like an Australian millionaire," said Andy.

"Correct."

"Stop agreeing with me," said Andy. "It doesn't stimulate conversation." He was pleased to see John smile.

"Now, tell me about everything," said Andy. His seriousness registered with John, who stopped chuckling.

"I've been forced to make a fundamental choice," he said.

"What alternatives?"

"Alice or Marilyn," said John defiantly.

"God," said Andy, with a theatrical groan.

"I mean it," said John. "You don't know what it's like living with Alice. She's a lovely girl and everybody envies me but they don't have to go to bed with her. She's made me a gibbering neurotic. She thinks that sex is filthy and repulsive and that I'm an animal. At one stage she had me thinking that I was violating her with lust. What bloody rubbish! I love her ..." He seemed surprised by what he had said, and his flow of speech petered out.

"That's the point," said Andy. "You love her. And she loves you. She told me so."

"But how can two people live together like that?" said John helplessly. "It's got to the stage where I *can't* make love to her, and she *doesn't* want me to. It's an impossible situation."

"All right. It's impossible. But you said you had made a decision. What is it?"

"I'm going to divorce Alice."

"Oh. And then?"

John toyed with his drink. "I'm going to marry Marilyn."

"You bloody imbecile."

"Look Andy, with Marilyn I'm happy. HAPPY!" He pounded the bar so hard that the drinks bounced. "We have a fantastic relationship!"

"And an expensive one," said Andy swiftly.

John shook his head with exasperation. "What are you complaining about? You're the one who explained her to me! She's a professional."

Andy lapsed into silence, sitting motionless.

"What does Marilyn think of this brain-wave?" he asked.

"She's agreeable," said John. "She says that we'll probably have to move to another country. You know, start afresh."

"She's sensible," said Andy. "She knows what it would be like if you were to get married and lived in *this* city." He gave a snort of derision. "Picture it. You walk into the Mayoral reception with your beautiful wife on your arm. And half the men realise that they laid her on their last out-of-town trip.

"Watch it, Andy!" said John. "I'm not going to let you debase Marilyn with your cynicism."

"Believe me, John," said Andy, "I may be a playboy, as you've so often told me, but at least I have more experience of women and sex than you. So listen. Marilyn is a whore. Alice is a wife. They are different animals and they can't swop places. Marilyn is an artist in bed. She's like a pro of ancient Greece, or a Japanese Geisha. She has a place in society, and by all means use her. But you must be out of your mind if you want to marry her!"

"Marilyn has agreed," said John stubbornly. "She loves me." He looked at his friend. "Does that surprise you? That a professional lady should fall in love with a customer? Anyway, it's happened. I'll take her away from that life."

"Come away from the squalor in which you live," said Andy sarcastically, "to the squalor in which I live." He lifted a placatory hand to John's anger. "Do you seriously think that a woman like Marilyn, who's had a dozen different men a week for five years, will be able to settle down to you, and only you, week after week, month after month, year after year? You obviously mean a lot, or she wouldn't have agreed to go with you. But there's always the possibility that she's using you, in cold blood. You know the logic: He's nice in bed, and he has a nice bank balance. As there's nothing to lose, for a while ..."

The savage words cut into John Mackenzie.

"You bastard," he said, the words barely audible. "You bastard." He began to sob. The wracking sound of a man crying. "What am I to do?" he asked. "There's no way out."

Andy grabbed him by the shoulders, firmly. "There's always an answer," he said, comfortingly.

CLINICAL DIAGNOSIS

Encouraged by Andy, who had played such an important part in his emotional problems, John Mackenzie discussed his dilemma with me.

With Andy prompting his memory, he related the development of his relationship with Alice, leading to their marriage, their lack of communication in bed and finally, his affair with Marilyn, his sexual fulfilment with her and his resultant infatuation.

When Mackenzie first made love to his wife it was, in his own words, a transcendental experience. Mackenzie was a man with a great sexual potential. But he was also an extremely sensitive man, conscious of every nuance of his wife's emotions. When he discovered, on honeymoon, that Alice's attitude during the sexual act was one of dutiful submission, he was appalled. He was experiencing ecstasy and naturally he wanted his wife to share it. Yet her facial expression showed that she was in the throes of disgust.

His desire subsided instantly. He was not the sort of person who could obtain sexual release without caring whether his partner was enjoying comparable pleasure. Mackenzie became impotent, unable to function sexually with his wife. But the impotence was only a symptom of Alice's attitude that made Mackenzie feel coarse and bestial. In a few months of marriage, Alice had conditioned her husband into consistent embarrassment and tension when they were in bed together.

Under specific circumstances, however, Mackenzie *could* function sexually with Alice. A case in point was the night Mackenzie invented an excuse to avoid attempting to make love to her. Alice assumed he had lost interest in her and that he had found another woman. She began to cry—and showed that she was vulnerable. Mackenzie was touched. He consoled and reassured her. Then he made love to her. In the process of reassuring his wife that he loved her and no one else, Mackenzie experienced the exchange of tenderness which, for him, was a necessary preface to the sexual act.

But after functioning successfully, he was disappointed when Alice gave no sign of pleasure or approval. Her lack of response on that occasion finally established Mackenzie's pattern of inadequacy with his wife.

The answer to Mackenzie's problem was soon to appear in the form of Marilyn. He was able to relax and relate to this girl. She was a voluptuary whose approach to sex was professional. Mackenzie discovered his sexual potential. Unfortunately, Mackenzie over-reacted. He became infatuated with Marilyn, who had served as a surrogate wife by teaching him the degree of satisfaction possible in bed. But Marilyn was not unique, although by all accounts she was certainly an expert, sexually.

I persuaded Mackenzie that it was not he who had a problem, it was Alice. But Alice was not culpable, she was propagating a distorted and destructive doctrine instilled in her by her mother. I told John he had never, at any time, suffered from impotence, but his wife, Alice, was being frigid. I emphasised strongly to Mackenzie that it was not possible to achieve any form of success by speaking to one partner in a marriage. Alice would have to join the discussion.

John was aghast at the prospect of including his wife in a discussion on sexual matters. He was sure that she would never agree. I insisted that it was imperative if he really wanted to save his marriage. He was extremely pessimistic, but he agreed to make the attempt. A few days later John telephoned to say that after a lot of persuasion and several arguments, Alice had consented to see me. The three of us met. Alice was obviously not at ease, but she was an intelligent woman who was clearly making a determined attempt to cope with a major problem.

I explained to her that John and I had discussed their sexual relationship with frankness, and I recapitulated our conclusions. I pointed out that it was possible to apportion the blame for the unfortunate state of affairs which had developed.

"What do you mean?" asked Alice.

"I mean that, in a way, a crime has been committed. But we know the criminal."

"Who?" asked Alice and John, virtually in unison.

"Alice's mother," I said.

Alice stared at me, white-faced and tense.

"Alice's mother told her, again and again, that a sexual relationship was obscene and dirty. She made her believe that a woman should only tolerate sex in marriage because of her duty to bring children into the world. The possibility of pleasure during the sexual act was eliminated by the concept which Alice's mother planted in her mind."

Alice listened intently as I asked her to accept that her mother's attitude was utterly wrong, and indescribably harmful. I put it to her that her husband was a normal man and that his demands were not excessive. On the contrary, from what I had been told, her husband was sensitive and considerate in his love-making.

We began to discuss love-making, and the total accept-ability of oral sex and love-play. I explained that anything pleasurable is permissible in a love bond. I described various love techniques in frank terminology.

Alice, still listening with intensity, began to weep. The tears streamed down her cheeks and she rushed out of my consulting rooms. John Mackenzie was upset and so was I, for Alice had impressed me as an intelligent woman seeking the truth. Mackenzie left, despondent about any prospects of improvement in his marriage. A few days later I had a telephone call—from Alice.

"May I come and see you?" she asked.

"Of course," I said.

"I want to see you without John knowing. Would that be all right?"

"Yes," I said. "Come in and we'll talk about it."

When Alice arrived for her appointment she apologised for having lost control of herself previously.

"I felt I must come and see you privately," she said. "I wasn't upset by what you were saying last time. But I realised that John would probably think, in the future, that anything I did while we were making love would be because of our conversation with you, and that it would not be originating from me."

She then asked me to explain to her precisely what she should do to afford her husband the greatest degree of sensual fulfilment. We had a fruitful discussion and Alice left, full of determination.

I heard nothing from either of them for several months. Then John Mackenzie came to see me.

"You know," he said, "that day when the three of us sat here, discussing things, we only really touched the surface. But you would be amazed at the benefits that talk has produced in our marriage."

"Would I really?" I said, smiling appreciatively at his delight.

"Confidentially," he said, "Alice is as good as Marilyn ever was. And what's more, I think she even enjoys it as much!" Mackenzie left. A happy, contented man.

At a later stage I met Alice again. She admitted that her whole attitude had changed. After our talk she *had* set out to please John during love-making, but at first could not eliminate repugnance. She had to act in order to convey her enjoyment. Quite soon, however, she began to enjoy herself genuinely. The important aspect was the tremendous fulfilment she experienced through causing her husband pleasure.

Many years previously, Alice's mother had unwittingly planted the seeds of destruction in her daughter. After unnecessary anguish and conflict, we uncovered the deed and nullified its effect. John and Alice Mackenzie were now able to enjoy married life.

4: The Sun Worshipper

"Mary! Come on! You'll be late for Mass!" Her sister's voice slowly became distinguishable to Mary, enveloped in the comfort of her Sunday-morning bed. Gradually she stirred, and awakened to the noises of her home.

Eileen, at fifteen, her younger sister by a year, was up early, eager to participate in church rituals. Mary smiled to herself, a little cynically. It wasn't so long ago that she, too, observed all the Saints' days, made the Stations of the Cross and novenas to Our Lady. But in the past year she'd lost her fiery sense of religious sanctity.

Now, the rituals seemed tedious—although she dared not mention such a sacrilegious thought in a household as devoutly Catholic as hers.

They went to Mass at St Peter's, Eileen chattering to her during the long walk.

The sermon was by a guest speaker, Father Valentine, a Dominican priest. Mary admired the Dominicans for their cool intellectualism and their sense of the dramatic. They were like disciplined actors, but their expression and delivery was put to the service of the Lord. Why, thought Mary mischievously, he even looks like Laurence Olivier.

Father Valentine was inveighing against the evils of birth control. He said that the natural genius of the human mind was being used to subvert the essence of the meaning of mankind's existence—the propagation of the species to the greater glory of God.

Mary was conscious of intellectual rebellion at the prospect of an endless series of unnecessary pregnancies. She was the eldest child in her family, and she could hardly remember her mother when she wasn't 'expecting'.

Regiments of babies' bottoms and phalanxes of nappies marched through her memory. Noise, uproar, confusion, arguments, tears and passed-down clothing ... these were the characteristics of their 'happy' family of seven children

93

which had impressed themselves on her. Eileen, she knew, didn't share her misgivings. To Eileen, they *were* a happy family. She loved the din and the togetherness.

After Mass, they went slowly back to their big, sprawling house. The younger children had already been to an earlier Mass. Now everyone gave a helping hand in the setting of the table and the preparation of Sunday lunch. Father, a venerable figure with humorous eyes, said grace, then carved the meat with dignity. The food circled the table and the family erupted into its customary noisy extroversion.

Mary ate quietly, and when she judged the moment, rose from the table. "Excuse me, Dad," she said. "I'm going to my room."

Her brother Johnnie, who was twelve, shouted to her: "Oh come on Mary! You know we're all going to the pool this afternoon. You never come with us any more."

The others joined the chorus. "Don't be a wet blanket, Mary." "Come on!" "What have you got in that room, anyway, that you're always going to?"

Mary found herself on the edge of tears. "I want to be on my own!" she shouted. "Can't you understand? I need some privacy!" She ran from the room, up the stairs, and flung herself on the bed. When her mother came to talk to her, a little later, Mary had recovered her composure. She explained to her mother that she liked being alone so that she could read.

That night, Eileen came to her room for a chat before they went to bed. She was talking about boys. "I'm not going to marry anyone handsome," Eileen announced with gravity. "They can never be trusted. I want a nice, ordinary man with manners and a sense of responsibility. Then we'll have lots of children."

"Not me," said Mary, so firmly that Eileen looked at her in surprise. "I won't have a big family. In fact . . ." she paused, astonished at her daring. "I wouldn't be surprised if I didn't even *have* any children!"

Eileen recoiled. "Mary!" she said. "What are you saying? You know it's a mortal sin to even think like that!"

She tried to sort out the theological tangle in her mind. "At least, I think it is."

"Rubbish," said Mary, emboldened that no lightning bolt had descended on her. "I don't see why a woman has to sacrifice her entire life to children. I want to live my own life."

She and Eileen never discussed the subject again. Eileen had decided that that sort of conversation was an occasion of sin and she avoided it.

Soon after she left high school, Mary met John Williams, a young man with whom she established an instant rapport. He was a little older than Mary, and in a few years would qualify as an accountant. They had so much in common that Mary found it uncanny. They liked the same sports—tennis and skating—and they both read a great deal, even sharing enthusiasms for the same authors. In her excitement at meeting her perfect man, Mary forgot to find out his religious beliefs. In any event, religion meant less and less to her.

She brought John home for Sunday lunch and after the usual procedure of grace, and the ritual carving, they settled down to the meal. Afterwards, they sat in the lounge. They had eaten so well, the conversation was desultory and relaxed. The group consisted of Mary and John, Mary's father and mother, and Eileen. The younger children had all rushed off.

After the usual exploratory questions, always expected when a daughter brings a young man home for the first time, Mary's father looked in a kindly way towards John.

"What is your religion, my boy?" he asked.

"I'm a Presbyterian," said John cheerfully. "Because of my Scots descent, of course." He put down his coffee cup. "I must admit, though, I haven't actually been to church for years."

Mary's father said nothing, but at the word Presbyterian, he looked at Mary and their eyes met. It seemed to Mary that her father was accusing her, wordlessly. Later, she persuaded John to take her for a drive. When she returned, her father called to her.

"Now, Mary," he said, recognising defiance on his daughter's face. "I'm not going to criticise you. I just want to give you advice, and believe me it's good advice, even though it comes from your father. John is a fine young man. Anyone can see that. But he's a Protestant and you're a Catholic. No good can come from such a friendship."

"Oh, Dad," said Mary. "He's just a friend. We've got lots of common interests and I like his company."

"Today's friend is tomorrow's husband," said her father. "You have a duty to your unborn children. You know that it's your moral duty to bring them up in the faith. Who knows whether a Protestant—a Presbyterian, at that—would agree to allow his children to be educated in a religion which he doesn't follow."

Mary's father paused. "Of course, if he wanted to convert, that would be a different matter."

"Father!" said Mary. "You talk as though John and I are getting married next week. Anyway, he hasn't even asked me!"

"Oh yes?" said her father. "So marriage *is* in your mind."

Covered in confusion, Mary stammered: "It's nothing like that! Can't two people just like each other?" She ran to her room and slammed the door.

Her relationship with John deepened, and she continued to see him, despite repeated warnings from her parents. One night, they went to dine at one of the most expensive restaurants. She could sense that something was in the wind. John bought champagne and they danced closely for hours. Later, he parked the car. Her intuition told her: Now's the moment! She was right. John proposed and she accepted.

That night she felt she had to ask John one key question. It had loomed so large in her mind recently she was terrified that this new wonderful period of her life, in which she had found a genuine partner, could be shattered by his refusal to agree. She took John's hand. "I know this may sound awful, darling, but I have to tell you."

"Come on then, what is it?" asked John, smiling at the thought of anything awful emanating from Mary.

"I don't want to have a family." She studied him for any sign of disapproval. To her amazement, he burst out laughing.

"That's fantastic, I was going to say exactly the same thing to you, but I was worried how you would react. Lots of girls think it's their duty to have kids. But I think it's criminal to bring them into the world the way it is. Anyway, if we had children we'd be wasting the best years of our lives looking after them."

The problem which had assumed such proportions to Mary, proved to be no problem at all. They announced their engagement, and after a short while were married in a non-denominational chapel. Mary's family were outraged and upset, but soon after the wedding John arranged a transfer to another town. Married life proved happy, uncomplicated and tranquil. At first, Mary was troubled by having to take precautions for sexual intercourse, but with her husband's help she was able to overcome the influence of her upbringing and they enjoyed a full and vigorous sex life.

In later years they joined a bridge club and this provided a social focal point for them. John did well at work, and was eventually made a partner. Their lives were full and happy.

Mary reached the change of life but did not suffer the menopausal anguish which afflicts some. She adjusted well, and easily.

One Sunday, she and John decided to go out for afternoon tea. They found a charming country café, and chose a table outdoors. It was a perfect summer's day. They ordered tea, scones and jam. They discussed the bridge convention scheduled for the following week and John told her of the latest scandal concerning one of his partners' wives.

Mary's attention was distracted by a buzzing sound. She looked for the source of it. There, in the jam, was a bee, struggling to free itself. She was seized by an unreasonable fear of the bee as she looked at it. It seemed to swell and

97

grow bigger. Progressively, as though inflated by some invisible force, it grew and grew until it became a giant. A ferocious beast that would attack her. The buzzing became a roar in her ears.

Mary screamed and leaped from her chair, knocked over the table, the tea-pot, the cups, her cigarettes, lighter and handbag. The tranquillity was shattered. Screaming, sobbing and shouting, Mary ran for the shelter of the café indoors. She had to escape from that monster.

Horrified, John ran after her, trying to comfort her. But as soon as she was safe indoors, beyond the bee's reach, Mary recovered and became her normal self. She apologised to everyone for the scene. She was terrified of bees, she explained. She didn't mention that she had only just discovered this fear.

They drove home. Mary felt embarrassed by her extraordinary performance. But John, tactful as ever, turned it into a joke. After a few days they forgot the incident.

A week later, on the following Sunday, John took Mary to the coast where they had recently purchased a small holiday cottage. After lunch, they took a rug to the beach and lay down to sunbathe.

As she was dozing off, Mary glimpsed a colourful shape. She opened her eyes. It was a wasp, brilliantly striped, and it was on the rug near her.

Mary went hysterical, leaped to her feet and ran blindly down the beach. Her voice went into its upper register— screams of total terror. Again her husband pursued her. He knew now that the first thing he must do was to take her indoors. In the safety of the cottage she instantly became normal, but she was shivering and shocked. He wrapped a blanket around her, and they drove home.

Next time John suggested an outing, Mary invented a headache. She couldn't expose herself to another ordeal as upsetting and embarrassing as that last incident.

For months, Mary had been having disturbing dreams. Most of them she forgot as soon as she woke, but one persisted. As the weeks went by it occurred more and more frequently. Finally, she had the same dream every night. There was nothing frightening or weird about the dream and Mary could not understand why she had it so frequently. She mentioned it to John who said that everyone had odd dreams from time to time.

The dream always took the same form. She would be on a beach. White sand stretching to the horizon. The sea brilliant blue, lapping against the slope of the sand. A small figure would appear, walking towards her. A child. A boy wearing tiny swimming trunks and a huge pair of sun-glasses. He would nod to her and walk on until his minute figure became invisible in the distant heat haze. Mary would wake feeling deeply disturbed, without understanding the reason for her anxiety.

Mary's behaviour pattern began to change. Every time there was the prospect of a journey, she managed to find an excuse to avoid it. She even arranged for shops to deliver all the household requirements. By the time the summer ended, Mary had organised her life so that she need never set foot outside the front door. Her fear of bees and wasps had become a full-time phobia.

John was concerned and upset but Mary would not even play bridge, unless friends would come to their home. Being a kind husband, John pandered to her wishes and they became homebodies.

When winter arrived Mary was the first to suggest that they go out. "There aren't any bees or wasps about," she explained to her bewildered husband. "You don't see them in cold weather."

That winter, Mary and John lived their lives as they had done for so many other contented years. In fact, Mary seemed more radiant and fulfilled than ever. Hopefully, John assumed that her phobia was a transient thing ... perhaps a belated symptom of menopausal hysteria. He was wrong!

They were strolling through town on their way to a bridge club meeting. The first hint of spring was in the air. Suddenly Mary stopped and clasped her hands to her ears.

"Stop it!" she shouted. "Stop it! For God's sake!"

"What is it, darling?" cried John. "Tell me!" He tried to wrench her hands from her ears.

"I can hear it! It's an enormous bee. It's going to get me!"

He held Mary to him, to comfort her, but her eyes rolled and she fainted. Thoroughly alarmed, John lifted her and ran to the car which was parked nearby. For the first time he was truly worried. There had been no bee in sight or within hearing distance. Everything had been in Mary's imagination. In the safety of the house, Mary insisted she had heard the bee. "That means they're about again," she said, referring to wasps and bees.

John studied her, worry and concern on his face. "Does this mean you are going to stay in the house until next winter?"

She looked at him shame-facedly.

"It's ridiculous, isn't it," she admitted. "But I'm so terrified of those things. If you only knew what I feel when I see them or hear them . . ." She shuddered.

John was silent. Was his wife an incurable neurotic? He knew he could not face another winter virtually confined to his home. He had friends and business acquaintances he needed to meet socially. He looked at his wife who was silently crying. They were so close, she could read his thoughts.

"It's awful, John, isn't it?" she said. "But what can I do? Isn't there someone who can help me . . .?"

CLINICAL DIAGNOSIS

The human mind is a thicket of confusion and treachery. It is the most bare-faced liar when it comes to telling the truth about itself. It hedges and prevaricates, erects mental booby traps, lays false trails, camouflages, confuses and doubles back on its tracks. All to hide an unpleasant truth . . . and in the process creates greater unhappiness, illness and mental anguish than could be caused by its directly facing up to the original source of the trouble.

An experienced psychologist is needed to sift fact from fancy, truth from invention, and feed back correct information into the mind. This pattern of self-deception produces amazing results, particularly in phobias. People with phobias are usually ashamed of the symptoms and hide these fears from others.

It is not uncommon for women to confine themselves to their homes for years on end, without their families realising that they are afraid to leave the safety and security of the house. Fears and phobias are extraordinarily varied. We all know of people who are terrified of lifts, or trains, or who cannot tolerate cats, dogs, snakes or spiders. Most of us don't realise that a multitude of people experience abject fear at the mere mention of mice, dirt, strangers, flowers, darkness, death or insanity. We might be tempted to laugh at people who are afraid to touch hair, or velvet, or a tennis ball or a carpet.

Phobic subjects fear ridicule nearly as much as the phobia itself. Most of them suffer in silence, rather than declare their troubles. This creates more distress. They hide their unhappiness to such an extent they develop the fixation they are mentally disturbed. It is a surpassing relief when they meet other patients with similar apprehensions and realise they are far from unique.

Many adults have mild fears about heights, lifts, aeroplanes, walking under ladders and going near 'haunted' houses. But these are small fears easily accommodated in the normal pattern of living. It is the abnormally intense fear which is termed phobia. These fall into distinct categories and can disrupt a person's entire life.

The commonest phobia is agoraphobia, which has many ramifications. Sufferers are not only afraid of open spaces: they cannot go shopping, or visit the cinema or theatre. They are afraid they might faint in public. They are nervous on journeys, or when left alone—yet, they are not at ease in crowded places. They often cannot bear the thought of a surgical operation. They don't like crossing streets. Obviously these people cannot function normally in a modern city. So they simply stay at home.

More than seventy per cent of agoraphobiacs are women, in which the complaint usually manifests itself between the ages of fifteen and twenty-five. When they are married their affliction can have a most distressing impact on the family circle. Because they find it difficult to confess their fears, their own family thinks of them as odd, or lazy, or lacking in will power. Agoraphobiacs are often sexually frigid, and prone to sexual disorders.

Phobias often involve a play on words—a form of punning. Female agoraphobiacs might have strong sexual tendencies which they suppress. But when they describe their symptoms they unconsciously reveal the true motivation. A woman may say she is afraid of 'going too far' when travelling on the tube. Or, on a train, she is 'afraid of going off the rails'. She is struggling to control her strong sexual impulses. More than likely she has been brought up by rigid, moralistic parents, to believe that natural impulses are sinful and wicked.

Mary Williams proved to be one of the most difficult and obscure cases I have treated. Yet, when we discovered the truth, and she was able to recognise it as such and emotionalise the situation, her phobia was cured with speed and simplicity. It was a textbook example of how the brain can deceive.

Mary was in her mid-forties when she came to see me. I obtained the basic information about her background—staunchly Catholic and sternly prohibitive—the sort of home in which a girl is led to believe that it is her obligation to marry and have as many children as possible. Clearly, Mary had rebelled against the influences brought to bear upon her in her formative years. She had broken away from the formal observance of her religion and had gone so far as to marry a Protestant. Throughout her married life she practised birth control. She bore no children. Then, she reached the change of life and the possibility of child-bearing disappeared.

Mary Williams insisted that she had no regrets about being childless. At first, her case baffled me. I tried various

102

techniques for the treatment of her phobia, but she did not respond. I tried to analyse her dream. Mary was still having her nightly vision of a child in swimming trunks and a huge pair of sun-glasses, walking along a lonely beach.

I became aware of the pun in the dream.

Phobias are frequently characterised by a play on words and this case was typical.

'Son' and 'Sun'. Those two words represented Mary Williams's problem. In spite of her insistence to the contrary, her Catholic conscience troubled her. She had not had a *son,* so her conscience decreed self-punishment by depriving her of the *sun.*

Bees and wasps were merely mental trickery to keep her away from the sun. Typically, her mind had 'cheated' away from the correct source of the trouble. It had seized upon bees and wasps as sun symbols. After all, bees and wasps could only be encountered in spring or summer.

It would have accomplished little if I had merely explained the symbolism to Mary. She might have accepted the explanation on an intellectual level—but this would not necessarily diminish her phobia, which was emotionally implanted. It is also possible that she might have considered the explanation to be an absurd one. In either case, the results would have been unsatisfactory.

I encouraged Mary to exercise her powers of detection and discover for herself the mental tricks of her own mind. In the course of several discussions, I nudged her along the correct path of thought. Meanwhile, I told her emphatically that once *she* found the answer she would be cured.

Mary finally linked 'sun' with 'son'. It was an extremely dramatic moment. Mary wept with the emotionalisation of her grief and guilt; at the same time she laughed with delight at having uncovered the source of her phobia.

Mary was able to face the truth, and realise how deviously her mind had protected her from guilt feelings. She accepted guilt, in terms of her upbringing, but realised that nothing now could be done about it. "If you believe you are guilty," I told her, "then feel guilty. But don't try to hide the truth from yourself." The phobia disappeared. Mary and her husband have a happy and successful marriage once again.

Another interesting phobia case was that of a woman of twenty-six who came to see me in Britain in November, when snow was imminent. Whenever she saw snow this young woman became hysterical. She would cower in corners, filled with dread—although she was unable to say what she was afraid of. In the winter months she was unable to leave her home. She would draw the curtains and never dare to look outside. She and her husband were desperate to find the cause of this irrational fear.

The phobia first manifested itself when she was sixteen. She'd been to many doctors. They gave her tranquillisers, to no avail. Then she graduated to psychiatrists—who interpreted her fear as a passing phase associated with the problems of adolescence. As soon as winter passed, the young girl was able to live a perfectly normal life during spring, summer and autumn.

I accept phobic patients only if they are good hypnotic subjects because then I believe we stand a good chance of uncovering the hidden problem. Experience has shown me that eighty per cent of people with phobias have unusually active imaginations—this, fortunately, makes them good hypnotic subjects. If it proves impossible to uncover the source of the phobia, I can then use hypnotism to condition the patient against his or her fear.

If a woman has a phobia about mice, for instance, I place her in a deep hypnotic state and tell her there is a mouse on the floor. If there really were a mouse, she would become hysterical. But because she is hypnotised, she is subconsciously aware that it is her imagination which is creating the mouse on the floor. Her fear is lessened. The 'mouse' becomes manageable. Gradually I increase the number of mice. Ten mice, one hundred. Then a thousand mice, crawling over her body, tangled in her hair. Finally she can handle the concept of thousands of imagined mice.

When I bring her out of her hypnotic state, the patient is able to encounter *one real* mouse with equanimity.

In the case of the snow phobia, we effected a cure in record time. The girl was an excellent subject for hypnosis and went immediately into a deep trance.

I asked her: "Remember the time you were *first* frightened by snow." At once she began to scream hysterically. She threw herself on the floor crouched under my desk with her hands in a protective attitude over her head. Her leg was twisted in an awkward position.

I told her I would awaken her and when I did so she must remember everything.

When she was conscious, she told me, in a highly emotional manner, how her phobia started.

At fifteen she was in a car with friends, on the way to a party. The car skidded on an icy road and crashed into a house. Her male companion and the boy driving the car were both killed. At the moment of impact she was thrown out of the car into a snowdrift, breaking a leg.

Typically in cases of this nature, it was not really the snow she feared. It was the icy road, and the wrecked car which created the terror. But her mind had focused on *snow* as the interlinking symbol. The accident was such a painful experience that she had blocked the experience from her conscious mind for over ten years. It was a full year after the accident, when she saw snow *again*, that her phobia showed itself for the first time. Of course, the one year time lag completely hid the source of the problem.

We achieved an immediate cure in this case. After that winter had passed, the young woman's husband phoned me to say that she had no recurrence of the phobia.

5: Not Such a Model Girl

George Wilson was a zealous amateur photographer.

"Move a little to the left, Susan," he asked his wife. She inched to the side. She and her husband's brother, Ralph, were situated on either side of Cathy, her three-year-old daughter, who was smiling into her father's camera. Already, at three, she was a veteran of photographic sessions. Her father chronicled every stage of her development.

"You're as pretty as a picture, darling," said George to his daughter. It was the sort of well-worn phrase, yet totally apt, which came to mind whenever he glanced at Cathy. She was almost too pretty, with her corn-flower blue eyes, retroussé nose and smattering of freckles. It was the kind of face which was a must to anyone with a camera.

"Just a minute," said Susan. She abandoned her pose and walked to the camera on its tripod. She had a commanding air which made her distinctive in any gathering. She radiated confidence. Susan peered at the camera. "Hmmm, I thought so. You turned the dial when you fitted the new filter. It would have been under-exposed." She twirled the mechanism until the setting was right.

"Thanks, darling," said George.

The viewing area of the camera seemed to give an extra dimension of clarity. Mother and child, he thought. What beauties. Susan's womanhood, her full mouth and alert, amused eyes, were the perfect counterpoint to the childish innocence of little Cathy. A pity Ralph had to be in the picture but he would have been offended if he'd been left out.

George shot a series of photographs as the trio smiled with determination.

"Right," he said. "Let's go outside with the cine-camera."

For an hour they improvised a melodrama, while George took several hundred feet of film. He filmed long-distance shots of Cathy, then zoomed in with the new lens he'd bought and took tight close-ups of her delicate features, making her look to left or right, smile, or be serious, according to the ragged plot.

That evening, they screened some of the footage just back from the processers. It showed their filming from the previous weekend.

"I saw an old Shirley Temple film the other day," said Ralph. "She's got nothing on Cathy. If Cathy and Shirley Temple were on the screen together, no one would even notice Miss Temple!" They laughed at Ralph's exaggeration, but George thought: It could be true!

"Let's have a look at you," said Cathy's mother. She inspected her daughter closely. Cathy was now seventeen. She stood dutifully while Susan tidied her hair and checked her make-up. "Sit down," said Susan, and Cathy sat.

"That's not the right shade of lipstick," said Susan, in a voice which brooked no opposition. For a moment Cathy had a fantasy ... she would wear purple lipstick, dye her hair green, refuse to wear any shoes at all and sweep into her birthday party on roller skates. She might even be naked.

"You really must try to remember the subtleties of colour combinations, Cathy," said her mother. "I don't know why, but you don't seem to be able to retain information, even when I spell it out for you so plainly." She sighed—a sound Cathy often heard.

"I don't think you should wear your hair down. After all you're seventeen now. If you wear your hair up you'll look more adult."

"Okay, Mum," said Cathy, and began to alter her hair.

"No," said Susan. "Leave it to me. I'll do it."

Cathy's arms were upraised to attend to her hair, but she let them fall and sat motionless as her mother busied herself with this all-important birthday party grooming.

"Oh, by the way," said Susan. "I didn't invite those two

boys you suggested. I made a few discreet inquiries. They're not the sort of people you ought to cultivate."

Cathy felt a pang of disappointment. "You mean Gregory and Peter?"

"Mmm," said her mother. "Why begin a friendship which is meaningless? They're not well-connected boys and there's no money there."

As her mother busied herself with her hair, Cathy speculated. In four years' time she would be twenty-one. She would be able to make up her own mind about her hairstyles, dress the way she wanted to, and invite whom she pleased to her parties. Thinking of parties reminded her of the music planned for tonight. Originally they were going to hire a mobile discotheque but her father hadn't thought that a good idea.

Instead, they decorated the lounge and gave it the atmosphere of a discotheque with subdued lighting. Mum and Dad had gone into town and chosen a selection of records. Cathy only hoped the music wouldn't be too square.

Her father put his head in the door. "Come along," he said. "Your guests are beginning to arrive." He put his hand on Cathy's shoulder. "I've been looking at the latest issue of *Now* magazine. They're running a contest for the teenage girl of the year. I've decided to enter you. With your looks I don't see how you can fail. The prizes are fantastic and you'll make an appearance on TV and a top modelling school will give you a free course. The clothes alone are worth five thousand."

"Please, Dad," said Cathy in a vaguely protesting manner. "You talk as though I've already won it. There will be thousand of entries."

"You're pretty as a picture, darling," said her mother reassuringly. "That's all that counts."

Rob Stephens and Joe Ross turned into the tree-lined avenue. 'What's that number again Rob?" said Ross, the photographer. He was driving the battered office car.

"It's that one, third on the left," said Ross, checking the address in his notebook.

"Miss Cathy Wilson, Teenager of the Year. Ten thousand in prizes just for having a photogenic face," said Stephens, the reporter.

"Beauty contests are a load of hogwash," said Ross. "Those beauties in *Playboy*, who list all their hobbies, like studying the origins of Mongolian Yaks. They take off their clothes and do as the photographer says, then the caption writers make up the personalities. This way is more honest. We sift through 50,000 photographs and choose the best looking."

"Okay, Joe," said Stephens. "Spoken like a true photographer. A picture cannot lie. You know and I know that *that's* a lie, already."

Both the reporter and photographer, two of the bright young men from *Now*, were looking forward to this assignment. They were to arrive unannounced at the Wilson home, inform Cathy that she had won the magazine's contest, and photograph her reactions.

Ross and Stephens were a good team. Stephens had a smooth line in conversation and women were captivated by his good looks. He would distract the subject's attention and Ross would trigger his Leica. When they began their partnership for the magazine, Stephens felt like a voyeur when he saw photographic spreads capturing a celebrity's embarrassment or a nonentity's private grief.

Now, he enjoyed the challenge presented by each new situation.

They rang the bell and waited. "Nice middle-class house," said Rob. "He's a grocer, you know."

"The old man?" said Ross.

"Yes. And he's mad about photography. He took all the pics of his daughter. You should have seen the selection he sent in."

They were asked into the house. Susan Wilson arrived and Stephens introduced his colleague and himself. "We're from *Now*," he said.

"Oh, of course," said Susan, her eyes lighting up. "Is it about the contest? She hasn't won, has she?"

"Yes, but please don't tell her yet," said Stephens hurriedly.

"Of course not, you want to photograph her surprise. I understand. Just wait here while I fetch her."

Stephens remembered that this woman was married to an enthusiastic amateur photographer. It helped when you were dealing with someone who understood journalistic requirements. He heard her calling upstairs to her daughter. "Come down, Cathy. Wear the new blue dress. You'd better keep your hair down. Hurry! I want you to meet some people."

Stephens looked at his colleague. "You can see who's top sergeant," he commented softly.

"Please sit down," said Susan, reappearing. "What can I get you. Tea, coffee. Perhaps a drink?" They settled for a beer.

Five minutes later they heard Cathy's door close and her footsteps. "Tell her now," said Stephens and the three of them walked to the foot of the stairs.

Cathy looked down at her mother and the two young men. She paused in insecurity. What was happening? "Come down, darling," said her mother. "Don't be nervous."

She moved down the stairway. "You've won the *Now* contest Cathy," said her mother. "You came first in the whole country."

Stephens heard the click of Ross's shutter. He was watching the young girl on the stairs, alert for every reaction. She looked stupendous, brilliantly blue eyes set off by a head of jet black hair. Stephens waited for the little shriek, the hands to the lips, the quick tears of delight. There was a formula to this situation, and everyone followed it, as though rehearsed.

To Stephens' astonishment, it didn't come. She looked frightened! he thought. She was looking to her mother as though waiting to be cued.

"She's delighted," announced her mother. "But she's a shy girl. She doesn't easily show her emotions. We've been worrying about this contest for months and now we're in

110

heaven. Mind you," she went on, herding them into the lounge, overriding the awkward moment with her charm and her flow of words, "I'm not really surprised. Cathy's looks are exceptional, or she couldn't have won. Could she? Come darling, give a winner's smile," said Susan. Stephens saw the young girl perform a smile, her lips moist, apart just the right distance, her eyes slightly angled. Ross's camera started clicking. The photographer circled the young girl, climbing on furniture, crouching on the floor, shooting spool after spool of film.

While the camera clicked, Rob Stephens began his practised technique of insinuating himself into the girl's confidence. If typical, she would at first be wary, guarded with her answers to casual questions and mistrustful. Then, as his sensitive approach got through, she would drop her guard and finally she would answer with the openness of a patient on a psychiatrist's couch. Stephens had done it before; he was confident he would do it again, particularly with an unsophisticated young girl like this.

He soon discovered that while Susan Wilson was present, he had no hope of establishing communication with Cathy. He would ask a question or throw out a statement, and Susan would answer, or pick up the conversational line. Cathy sat and smiled, looking arch, wan, wistful or vivacious on demand. Stephens tried to force the conversation, directing a straightforward question at the girl and looking her full in the eyes. Cathy would smile and look trustingly at her mother, who would reply.

The phone rang and Susan answered it. It was a long-distance call from her sister. At once, she began the story of her daughter's success. Stephens saw his chance. "Come on, Joe," he said, "let's get some pictures in the garden."

"Good idea," said Ross. He took Cathy by the arm with a photographer's proprietary right, and the trio went outside, where the setting sun filled the beautiful garden with soft light.

Cathy looked alarmed, but she obeyed the demands of the photographer. Stephens began his patter. He flattered her, complimented her on winning the contest and painted

111

a glittering picture of what it would mean to Cathy in terms of material gain and prestige.

"Now, Cathy," he explained, "what we're trying to do is catch you as a person, so that when the reader of *Now* puts down this magazine he will feel that he knows you personally.

"We'll start with simple things," he said. "For instance, what are your hobbies?"

"Hobbies?" said Cathy, and a look of desperation passed like a cloud across her eyes. "I ... er, I don't have any."

Stephens eyed her sharply. "Your entrance form ... it said you read a book a day ..."

Cathy coloured and looked confused. "Oh. Well, my father filled that in ... I didn't even see it."

"What about music?" Stephens tried again.

"Oh yes. I like it," said Cathy.

"What kind?"

"All kinds, you know ... just music ..." said Cathy helplessly.

"What about actors. Is there anyone you admire particularly?"

"I like Robert Redford," said Cathy, defiantly, thinking of the remark her father made the previous week when Redford came under discussion. "He's just a pretty face," said her father. Cathy hadn't argued. Now, she felt pleasure at this belated act of defiance.

"Hmmm. Nothing original about that," said Stephens. He was beginning to be worried. This girl was proving negative. The most difficult people to write about were the passive non-emotionals.

He and Ross were expected to produce a spread of dynamic photographs and riveting prose about one of the most exciting young beauties in the country. But you had to strike some spark from a personality before you could set light to your pen.

"What sports do you play?" he asked.

"I'm no good at sports," said Cathy. She added: "I'm not much good at anything, really."

112

"Come over here, Cathy," ordered Joe Ross. She obeyed, meekly, and he positioned her under a tree. He used a different camera and photographed her in a variety of poses.

Pictorially we're going to be okay, thought Stephens. Joe will have great shots. But I'm going to be in trouble. She has no interests and no opinions, except a very low opinion of herself.

"What about boyfriends," he said hopefully.

Cathy shook her head. "No. Not really," she said.

Rob Stephens decided to lean on her, hard. "Now don't be ridiculous, Cathy. Are you trying to tell me you have no interest in anyone, or anything?"

The beautiful young girl looked at him, her eyes like blue pools against the blackness of her hair. Suddenly they went moist and tears began to fall.

"I've been trying to tell you ..." she said, so softly he could barely hear her. "I'm useless ... I don't know anything." She bent her head and cried silently.

Mrs Wilson's voice came across to them from the house. "Cathy dear, I think you'd better come in now. It's getting chilly."

Cathy rose and walked between the two stunned young men, wiping her eyes. They walked along behind her.

Later, Stephens took Mrs Wilson aside.

"We had a very successful photographic session," he told her. "She's a fantastic model."

"But I need lots of personal information for my article," he said, "Cathy seems very ..." he searched for a suitably gentle word—"withdrawn ... sensitive. I haven't had any success in getting her to talk about herself."

"Cathy isn't very communicative," said her mother, with amusement.

"Joe Ross wants to take a few formal photographs of her in the studio," he said. "Tomorrow night, if that's all right. I thought I'd introduce Cathy to some of the girls on the staff and take them all to a late dinner after the photo call. That way she'll feel relaxed and I should be able to get the material I need."

Mrs Wilson nodded. "I'm sure that'll be fine. I'll speak to my husband tonight."

The newsmen left with Mrs Wilson in the doorway, waving cheerfully. A few feet behind stood her daughter, eyes downcast.

The photographic session the following evening was a great success. A couple of the girl staffers Rob had invited were enviously complimentary about Cathy's looks. Rob had briefed Fiona Davidson, a fashion writer, to relax Cathy and make her more at ease. She spoke often to Cathy during the photo call and, at the dinner later, sat next to her, with Rob on the other side. Now, Cathy had gone to repair her make-up and Fiona leaned across to talk to Rob.

"She's empty," she said with pleasant venom. "Honestly, Rob, I don't think there's anything there! She doesn't have any opinions about anything. All she can do is smile. I've met the type before. They think that being pretty is enough."

"The trouble is," said Stephens, "they're almost right."

He toyed with his drink. He had to have his copy through by noon the following day and he didn't want to invent an entire personality to fill the vacuum behind Cathy's stunning façade.

When the band played again he asked Cathy to dance. I'll try and get to her on a personal level, he decided. Might as well give it the old college try. At twenty-five he seemed almost old in comparison to this innocent teenager. To his surprise she was very different on the dance floor. She came to him willingly and he found her proximity exciting. Now he had a genuine interest.

"Come up to my flat for a while, Cathy," he said, expecting the usual protest about having to be home.

"All right," she said, obediently.

"When do you have to be home?" he asked.

"They expect me by twelve," she said.

"It's only 10.30," he said. "Let's go now." Cathy agreed.

Stephens parked his car and leaned over Cathy to unlatch her door. On impulse he turned his head and kissed her.

She didn't pull away so he put his arm around her and kissed her lingeringly. She tasted clean and fresh. He drew away and looked at her. "Thank you," Cathy said.

As he opened the door for her, Stephens thought unbelieving: She said, thank you! *I* make a pass and she says thank you! In his apartment he put on some music and poured drinks. Cathy had a coke. She'd had wine with her meal and her cheeks were faintly flushed.

Stephens saw her in an interior moment as she leaned back in the chair, her feet tucked under her, unaware that he was watching. She looked pleased, as close to animation as he had seen her. He could still taste her lipstick. He sat on the arm of her easy chair and kissed her again. She cuddled up to him as disarmingly as a puppy, soft, warm and sweet. He let his hand brush against her breast. Cathy kissed him with wholehearted enthusiasm. She made no move to push him away so he began to fondle her.

In a spirit of adventure, Stephens decided to find out how far she would go. He cupped her breasts in his hand and she put her arms around his neck with the affectionate simplicity of a child. He bared both her breasts and kissed them. She uttered soft sounds of pleasure.

His hand explored her with no resistance, no opposition. Using both his hands he began to remove her underclothing. At once she lifted her body to make it easier for him to strip the flimsy garments from her. Then she sat up and took off her dress in one swift movement.

Stephens was strangely shocked. He had made so much progress so swiftly in this seduction that he felt unsettled, like a general whose forces have battled forward expecting stiff resistance and encountered nothing. He picked up Cathy and carried her to the bed. As he laid her gently on the covers she held her hair while he placed the pillow under her head. The movement made her look like a traditional pin-up girl draped on a divan. He smiled and she smiled back, a stunningly beautiful girl with a perfect figure.

A short while later he discovered that Cathy was a virgin. This astonished him but did not deter him. They made love but when Stephens' first passion was spent he got up and dressed. The naïveté which had originally appealed to him, now repelled him. The fumbling sex act had been successful only on the basic level of relieving his physical needs. Now, he felt irritated by the girl, and her acceptance of his wishes and desires.

He looked at her, lying on the bed, unsure of what was expected of her.

"You'd better put on your clothes, Cathy," he said, pretending consideration.

He fixed himself a drink. Cathy dressed and sat next to him.

"So you were a virgin," he said softly.

She nodded. He was suddenly voraciously inquisitive about this strange young woman, his journalistic instinct prodding him to find out the whys and wherefores.

"Haven't you had any steady boys?" he asked.

"No," said Cathy. "Not really." She looked confused. "You know ..." and then she stopped.

"Come on, Cathy. Don't be afraid to talk to me."

"It's just that you're the first boy I've really been out with," she said.

Her childish use of the term 'boy' touched him.

"But that's impossible," he said. "In this day and age ... Don't your parents let you go out on your own?"

"It's just that ... my father is usually with me, and most of the time we take photographs when we go anywhere, and then I've been studying very hard." Cathy looked him directly in the eye. "This is the first time I've been alone with a boy. I suppose they let me come out with you because of the competition and everything."

Stephens noticed the girl was shaking. He realised that, to her, this was a crucial experience. She was trying to find words.

"Was I ..." she stopped and swallowed. Stephens put his hand on her arm. "Was I all right?" She couldn't bring herself to look at him.

"Of course, darling," said Stephens, lying courteously. "You were fine. And you'll see ... it gets better all the time."

116

She bent her head and kissed his hand, where he held her comfortingly. "Thank you," she said. "Oh thank you."

Embarrassment covered Stephens and he rose. "Come on, we have to get you home. It's nearly midnight."

He took Cathy home. The next morning he invented interesting and novel qualities and characteristics for Cathy Wilson—Miss Teenager of the Year. When he'd finished his piece, he sat back and slowly reread it. Then he put it down.

"Now *that's* the kind of girl I'd like to meet," he thought, chuckling.

Some years later Rob Stephens was on an assignment in the capital. After dining at the Press Club with a girlfriend he had not seen for some months. he agreed to her suggestion that they visit a night-club.

Stephens had never been to this club before but his partner, Lyn, a model, told him it had become the fashionable place for people in the arts. Many writers, actors and musicians frequented it. Lyn was obviously known there and they got a good table. Lyn began to point out personalities of interest. At one big table there was a group of beautiful girls. The men were older, with the slight arrogance of wealthy middle-aged businessmen.

The host was Giles Mancroft, a textile millionaire who had a reputation for enjoying his money. He backed plays and films and expected and received sexual perquisites from starlets and young actresses eager for fame. He was a florid man with an unpleasant smile which seldom left his face. He lifted his glass as Stephens watched, and proposed a toast. The party lifted their glasses, drank and resumed their rowdy conversation.

"Wait a minute," said Rob, interrupting Lyn's flow of malicious information. "Who's that girl, third from the left, facing us?"

"Oh, trust you," said Lyn. "How do you do it, picking them out from that distance? That's Cathy Wilson. I hear she's the most enthusiastic lay in town. And that's saying something!"

117

"Hmm," said Stephens. "What else does she do?"

"A model. Like me. That's probably how she came to the attention of Mancroft's crowd. Mind you, I'm not against sex, you know ..."

"I know," said Stephens, grinning.

" ... but I do draw the line at certain things. Mancroft and his mob go in for orgies ... Weekends at his mansion or aboard his yacht. I found myself at one of his little shindigs once but I managed to get out before it got too rough. With that lot, anything goes. The trouble with that sort of thing is that once you start, you have to keep going faster. More and more. Bigger and better orgies. Until nothing, but *nothing*, gives any kind of thrill."

"Okay, okay, Miss Morality," said Stephens. "It's just that I did a piece about that girl. When was it?" He thought back. "Four years ago. We selected her as Miss National Teenager. She was just eighteen then. Look at her now. Her mother said her face would be her fortune." He laughed. "It might have been better for her to have been born ugly."

He watched Cathy. She had lost the childish, unformed look of a teenager and she was dressed in adult sophistication. But as he kept his eyes on her he detected a familiar pattern, though he had not seen her for four years. She hardly spoke. She listened intently, and smiled almost constantly, giving her attention first to one side of the table and then the other.

He studied the other women in the party. They all had striking good looks. Money buys beauty wholesale, he thought. Not one of the girls was more than twenty-five, and they were all superb.

I wonder if she still says 'thank you', he speculated.

"Come on darling. Let's dance," said Lyn. They went to the floor and Stephens wondered if Cathy would recognise him. She did, at once, as he danced past and he was flattered. She smiled and waved to him and Lyn. Lyn gave an answering flutter of the wrist. "Well," thought Stephens, "at least it proves that a girl always remembers her first man."

118

Cathy had come to the party with Jack Robinson, one of Mancroft's aides. They had met that week at a fashion show and he invited her out. She stayed at his apartment overnight and he had invited her for a weekend outing with Mancroft. This was the beginning of that party.

"I hope you're a sport," Jack had said, looking at her with amused assessment.

"I hope so too," said Cathy.

"We get together sometimes like this coming weekend," said Jack. "Giles likes everyone to let their hair down."

"What sort of weekend will it be?" Cathy had asked. He grinned, and Cathy hastened to add: "I mean where will we go? Will we be in town, or what?"

"Giles has a country house. We'll start with a party in town, then move there later. We can drive back on Monday morning."

Since he had called for her this evening they had hardly exchanged a word. Jack was seated on the other side of the table, some distance from her. He was talking to a girl she'd never seen prior to this evening. In fact, everyone at the party was a stranger, except Giles Mancroft, whom she'd met previously at a fashion show.

Cathy had been overwhelmed when she saw the other women. They seemed so beautiful, never lost for words, and obviously they knew each other. She was grateful when, midway through the evening, one of the girls called Mary-Anne invited her to the powder-room. Cathy soon realised that Mary-Anne knew her way around.

"The thing to do, honey," said Mary-Anne, "is to enjoy yourself no matter what happens. They're all nice people, only some of them have kinky ideas. Go with the tide and you'll be okay."

Mary-Anne had asked Cathy how she came to be in the party. "At first I thought you looked like the odd one out," said Mary-Anne with brassy directness. "You know, you can't always tell with parties like these. But if you came with Jack that's okay. Where did he meet you?"

Cathy told her.

"And you say you met Giles a few weeks ago?"

"That's right."

Mary-Anne smiled. "That's the way it often happens. Jack is Giles's right-hand man in more ways than one."

"Oh," said Cathy. She didn't understand what was going on, but Mary-Anne said it would be all right and she seemed to know.

"So this is your first time at one of these little outings," said Mary-Anne, with what Cathy realised was her customary forthrightness. "Stick close to me and I'll clue you up on what's expected. Jack wouldn't have brought you if he hadn't felt you were a . . . well, a swinger." She smiled at Cathy with a sort of intimacy.

"Thanks a million, Mary-Anne," said Cathy. "I did feel pretty strange."

They arrived at Giles's country place at 2 a.m. Everyone was in a gay mood. There had been plenty of champagne and though Cathy had drunk very little, she felt deliciously irresponsible and uninhibited. They all went into the entrance hall of the great house. Cathy was impressed and awed. They went into a reception room, and Cathy saw that everything was prepared for a gathering. A cocktail bar was stocked high and the lights were comfortably low.

Another round of drinks was passed around and Cathy began to feel dizzy. She felt a hand on her shoulder. It was Mary-Anne.

"Come on, honey," said Mary-Anne. "Come with me." She led the way through the knots of people, chatting and drinking. It was like any other cocktail party, thought Cathy but she felt uneasy. Thank heavens Mary-Anne was being so nice. Jack seemed to be ignoring her. She tried to think of what she had done to upset him.

In the study, Mary-Anne locked the door and sat down, patting the place next to her in invitation to Cathy.

"Obviously you're game or you wouldn't be here," she said. "But when I think of my first time I still get the shudders. As long as you know the ground rules, there's not much that can go wrong."

"Go wrong?" said Cathy.

120

"I mean sometimes girls get hysterical because they haven't been warned ..."

"Warned against what?" Cathy began to feel distinctly apprehensive.

"Look baby, don't be so damned dumb," said Mary-Anne. "Stop acting like a Girl Guide. This weekend is a sex scene."

"Oh," said Cathy. She wasn't shocked, for after all she enjoyed sex. And anyway, that was all that interested men. You had to pander to their weaknesses.

"I'm just trying to make sure that you know what's going on." Mary-Anne continued. "Now, tonight's going to start off with Mr Mancroft's favourite little games. We'll all be together in the main hall with the lights off. And no clothes on, either."

"You must be joking," said Cathy.

"I'm dead serious. Old Mancroft says he enjoys the excitement of surprise—feeling around in the dark. They take out all the furniture so you can't bump into anything that will hurt you." Mary-Anne giggled. "It's all carpets and cushions."

"But ... but ... how do you know who ..." Cathy didn't finish the sentence.

"That's the whole point," said Mary-Anne.

"What happens later on?" said Cathy.

"After that, when everyone has loosened up, we do it with the lights on," said Mary-Anne.

"Oh," said Cathy. She felt sick. She thought: I'm going to walk out of here.

"Oh, don't look so bloody sad," said Mary-Anne. "We all do it and I promised you, you'll have a ball. Everyone does. You don't want to be the odd one out."

Mary-Anne had used that phrase again. The thought of being the odd one out sent a quiver of fear through Cathy. If I try and leave I'll make a fool of myself, she thought. Anyway, how can I get back to town? She thought for a second of taking a car. There was bound to be one with keys in the dashboard. I'd never get away with it, she thought despairingly.

A short while later there was a little eddy of excitement through the guests and men and women separated into two groups. Mancroft led the men through one door. The girls, squealing with excitement, went through another. Each group undressed, then entered the main hall.

When they closed the doors it was absolutely dark. The windows must be sealed, thought Cathy. She felt a hand clasp hers. It was Mary-Anne.

"Now don't worry about a thing, honey," said Mary-Anne, and kissed her. She felt Mary-Anne's tongue in her mouth. Then her hand began to move over her body. She felt the full warmth of Mary-Anne's body against hers, then rising passion. What's happening to me?—she heard a voice cry in her mind. What am I doing here? She wanted to scream for help. But who could she scream to?

"You were great, honey." It was Mary-Anne's voice.

She lay in the dark, letting the excitement ebb slowly. She was still breathing heavily. Around her she heard groans and sighs.

There was a hand on her. She touched it. It was hairy.

"Come here," said a male voice. Then she felt another pair of hands. Two men were with her, naked in the dark. Cathy felt her head swimming. I'm going to faint, she thought. Don't, she told herself. Don't make a fool of yourself. She lay in the dark, silently, while men and women she could not see writhed about her like animals.

Jim Bishop moved restlessly in his armchair and watched the television screen with half-hearted interest.

Women! he thought, and had another sip of the coffee his wife, Cathy, had just made for him.

Wife! That's a laugh. He thought back on their relationship. He'd met Cathy at one of Giles Mancroft's weekend parties. To him, she'd been the most strikingly beautiful woman in a gathering which included not one plain Jane. They had enjoyed the sexual excesses of the party and he dated her during the weeks following. She was not only beautiful, but remarkably eager to please and she seemed to want him constantly. She had a feminine glow which

122

warmed his masculine ego. They saw more and more of each other and Bishop, at the age of forty-five, decided he had finally found a woman with whom he could risk another mariage. His previous marriages had both ended in divorce.

Bishop was a wealthy man. He had inherited a going concern in the import-export line and sustained and improved it. Now, he was wealthy enough to hold his own with Mancroft and his friends. 'Work hard and play hard!' was Mancroft's motto and for some years Bishop had been an enthusiastic participant in the tycoon's imaginative sexual revelry.

Things changed when Cathy came along. This young, passionate girl, who needed him constantly for affection, began to fill the vacuum in his emotions which, until then, he had attempted to occupy with bawdry. What's more, she was literally ready for anything. If he needed to flog his jaded sexual appetites into life with some bizarre charade, he knew she would assist his enjoyment.

The first six months of their marriage went well.

Bishop drank his coffee and shook his head. He glanced at Cathy, absorbed in the late night programme. Until only a few months ago, Cathy at this hour would have dressed as provocatively as she could. Now, she wore a demure nightdress. She used to desire him constantly, a hand stroking his thigh, tickling his chest or scratching his back. He merely had to lift a finger and she would succumb to his sexual wishes.

He put the coffee cup down slowly, disturbed by his thoughts. He could not understand what had happened to Cathy in the past few weeks. She had undergone a metamorphosis of character which bewildered and stunned him. Previously, she would drink deeply from the sexual cup. Now she was a total abstainer.

Only the previous night, Bishop had made an effort to re-kindle the sexual flame which used to blaze between them. She rejected him with the pained dignity of a nun. Annoyed, Bishop badgered her for an explanation. Almost at once she broke down. She flung herself into his arms and through her tears he eventually extracted an explanation of sorts: "Can't you understand, darling," she sobbed, "I want you to love me for myself, not for my body!"

The words were so absurdly naïve he was left floundering. He'd protested, to no avail. "I want you because I genuinely love you. At the beginning, maybe, it was just sex, but now I love you. Believe me, Cathy, I do." He tried to convey his sincerity to her. To his surprise, he meant what he said.

She accepted his words, but in spite of that, he spent a restless night without the sexual release he had been accustomed to. The restlessness created irritation. He looked at his watch. He could be at the club in fifteen minutes. He could be in bed with any hospitable body within the same period of time. He'd been a sexual profligate all his life. Cathy couldn't expect him to become a celibate. He felt indignation. It was all Cathy's fault. Tonight, he would sleep with someone else. "I'm going out," he said.

Cathy looked at him despairingly, but said nothing as he slammed the door. She sat very still, oblivious to the noisy television.

He's going to sleep with someone else, she thought. The realisation had been as clear as if spoken. I'm forcing him into it, she accused herself. Then he'll leave me. She turned her head and saw her reflection in the mirror. Pretty, she thought. Pretty useless! Despair seeped through her. What's happening to me? Why have I gone off sex? The question loomed large, but she had no answer.

CLINICAL DIAGNOSIS

Cathy is a harrowing example of how doting parents can destroy a girl by doing everything *for* her.

Her father was so bewitched by his daughter's prettiness that he spent most of his time adoring her through the medium of a camera lens. He asked nothing more of his daughter than that she should look pretty.

Her mother was a dominant personality who anticipated her daughter in every situation. A hidden resentment of her daughter's 'young' beauty drove her to compete with her. Verbally she was always well ahead of Cathy. She and her husband fed the girl constantly with one-dimensional flattery ("You're pretty as a picture ... that's what counts"), but would not allow her the responsibility of decision-making. Her mother decided what dresses Cathy should wear, how she should style her hair and who her companions should be.

Up to the time of Cathy becoming a teenager she had never had the opportunity to formulate original thoughts, to hold opinions of her own. This was demonstrated when the reporter interviewed her for his magazine. She had no specific likes or dislikes, no strong views on any subject.

When the reporter pressed for a response, she finally broke down completely and described herself as 'useless'. At the same time, Cathy believed herself to be pretty. Her parents' constant assertions convinced her of this. Her two key concepts of herself were, therefore, 'pretty' and 'useless'. As her parents never allowed her to do anything for herself, she felt certain she was incapable of doing anything.

When Stephens invited Cathy back to his flat, he had no idea that this would be the first occasion in which Cathy would be alone with a man. When he kissed her in the car, she did not feign anger or reluctance. She was grateful that an attractive young man should think she was worthy of being kissed and so she said 'Thank you'.

When he tried to seduce her, she could only acquiesce. After all it takes a confident person to say 'No'. Cathy was so lacking in confidence, she was unable to hold back anything of herself. She gave totally, in self-denigrating gratitude for being wanted. And because she gave herself so unwithholdingly, men became bored with her. It is human to want what you cannot have, and to tire quickly when you achieve it too easily ...

When men used her, and abandoned her, she would assume they had left her because she was useless.

She succumbed to any sexual indignity rather than risk the accusation that she was not 'with it'. When she attended the orgiastic weekend party at Mancroft's house, and Mary-Anne befriended her, Cathy was inordinately grateful. When Mary-Anne proved to be a lesbian, and began to seduce her, Cathy's gratitude even conquered her instinctive revulsion against the act. It was as though she was paying Mary-Anne for her kindness.

When Cathy met Joe Bishop and he warmed to her childish eagerness to please, she was stimulated to an even more intense giving of herself. Bishop's primary emotional need was to feel wanted. He also enjoyed sexual excesses. So he married her.

In the early months of their marriage, Cathy continued playing her role, but with decreasing enthusiasm. Her lack of self-esteem and her self-destructive urge impelled her to drive her husband into the arms of another woman. She did this by withholding her body from him. The husband, of course, construed this as a sign that his wife no longer wanted him physically. It was only a short step away from a break-up of the marriage.

The irony of this relationship was that although it had its origin in sexual abandonment, it deepened into genuine love. Jim Bishop really loved his wife. Cathy recognised this new development. Then, because she realised that Bishop truly loved her, she wanted to be loved only for herself. She thought of sex as a means to an end—the end being the acquisition of love. Now that she had a husband, there was no need for sex. What's more, she wanted to prove Bishop's love for her by withholding her sexuality from him—to see if he would still love her.

This strategy failed and instead of drawing him closer to her, she alienated him. Then, she self-destructively forced him towards another woman—to see if he loved anyone else more than he loved her. Cathy had to learn the truth about herself before she could improve her emotional life. She had to be made aware of how her parents had unwittingly distorted her personality during her formative years. Once she accepted this, she was half-way to a cure.

When she consciously began to fight these influences, instead of reacting to situations in a silent, hidden manner, without communicating her desires and fears to her husband, she was able to save the marriage. She reached the point where she realised, in desperation, that by withholding herself sexually she was losing her man. She started to act rationally—she re-introduced her passionate sexual approach.

This was the final solution. Her husband could now love her sexually and as a person. Cathy found emotional maturity.

6: The Astonishing Tale of How Tommy's Twitch was Cured by Sloan's Liniment.

It was Tommy Twiller's first day away from home, and he was tearful. He didn't like the idea of school. In his five years, the only world he had known was his family. The only time he'd ever left home was to pay a visit to an aunt out of town, with his parents.

Now he was being taken to a place called school. He felt afraid and unsure, but his mother held his hand firmly.

"Once you've met all the other boys and girls you'll like school, Tommy. You'll make lots of friends."

Tommy didn't say anything, but kept a grip on his mother. When she handed him over to a teacher he managed not to cry, and then he was surrounded by so many new and interesting things that his attention became fully occupied.

The teacher was nice and showed him where to sit. There were children all around him—the first time he'd seen so many children together. He noticed that they looked at him a lot and he looked back at them. Some of the boys and girls seemed to be laughing at him and some became shy and looked away. Others spoke to him and told him their names.

After a while a bell rang and the teacher said it was play-time. They ran into the grounds of the school and Tommy explored the new sights and sounds. He was standing quietly under a tree, watching some children playing, when an older boy with two friends came up to him. He hadn't seen them before.

"What's your name?" said the bigger boy.

"Tommy," he said.

The boy and the other children began to laugh.

"There! He's done it again!" said one of them. "Hey that's funny!" said the big boy. "Come on, do it again for us."

Tommy didn't know what they were talking about.

"What are you laughing at?" he asked them, bewildered and close to tears.

The big boy turned and shouted across the playground to another group of children. "Hey! Come over here! See what we've found!"

"Leave me alone," cried Tommy, and the three boys burst out laughing again.

"His name is Tommy," said one of them. "Tommy the Twitcher! Twitchy Tommy!" He doubled up laughing.

By now all the other children had run over to see what the excitement was about.

"Please leave me alone," cried Tommy. "I haven't done anything." The tears welled in his eyes.

There was another roar of laughter, as though he'd said something funny. By now Tommy was afraid, and humiliated. He felt like a cornered animal. The boys circled him prodding him and jeering.

One boy, the school mimic, pushed his way to the front row of children. He watched Tommy closely, then threw his head grotesquely to one side, as though it was about to roll off, raised his shoulder convulsively and thrust his arm out spasmodically. The boys roared their approval.

"That's him, Jimmy" shouted a boy. "That's him exactly. The twitcher!"

Tommy turned and fled as fast as his legs would carry him. The other boys chased him like hounds after a fox, shouting, screaming and leaping with excitement. The biggest boy, the one who had first talked to Tommy, caught him, grabbed him around the waist and picked him up.

"I don't think Twitchy knows how clever he is," he said to the children. "Let's show him!"

Tommy, kicking, striking out and crying was picked up by the children and carried roughly to the toilets.

"There you are, Twitcher," said the big boy, and put Tommy down in front of a full-length mirror.

The children fell silent. They knew that this was going to be a specially cruel moment. They waited attentively.

Tommy looked at himself in the big mirror. He saw the shiny faces behind him.

He put his hand to his eyes and wiped away the tears so that he could see properly. He saw his head roll, his mouth open and close, like a fish blowing a bubble. His shoulders move jerkily and his arm fly out, as though he was trying to throw it away.

He was like the boy in the playground, who had moved in a funny way. But it's me, thought Tommy. I didn't know I did that. He saw the movement again. He began to cry, hysterically, and tried to run through the boys. They pushed him back laughing.

A teacher heard the commotion and went to investigate. He heard the boys chanting: "Tommy the Twitch. Tommy the Twitch!"

When they heard the teacher's voice, the chanting died and the children formed into groups and began to walk away. The teacher saw a small figure lying on the ground. It was Tommy. He had fainted. The teacher carried him to the dispensary.

"What happened to the child?" the nurse asked.

"They were teasing him because of his twitch."

"Kids!" She clucked her tongue. "They're savages."

The teacher shook his head. "The poor little chap should have bragged about his twitch. He could have been a hero and they would have been jealous." He looked at the nurse. "But it's too late for that now."

Tommy moved and opened his eyes. As the nurse and the teacher watched, consciousness returned and he began to twitch again, grotesquely. The nurse gasped, involuntarily. Tommy began to cry and they gave him a sedative. The nurse phoned his mother and she came at once to take him home.

Two weeks later Tommy had arrived home from school when his mother's sister Emily, came visiting. She'd brought an aeroplane which could be fired from a catapult. He ran about with the new toy, shooting it into the air and watching it glide to earth.

When he was out of earshot, Emily turned to her sister. "How's he getting on, Irene?"

Tommy's mother sighed. "I had a long talk with the school principal. He seemed to think there must be a reason for Tommy's spasm but I explained that he has *always* had it." She shrugged in frustration. "Who can say when it began? He's always been highly-strung and his twitch seems to have grown with him. Of course it becomes more noticeable when he's agitated, which is what happened on his first day at school."

The two women exchanged glances, remembering the anguish of that day.

"David and I had serious thoughts about keeping him away from school altogether and getting him private tuition. But the headmaster seemed to think that we were being negative. He said Tommy needed to mix with other children."

"Do the other kids still tease him?" asked Emily.

"Apparently he's now accepted. But they still call him Tommy the Twitch. As the headmaster said, it's something he'll have to learn to live with."

"What about the theory that it might be physical in origin?" asked Emily.

"We took him to a neurologist," said Irene. "There's no brain damage, so that's not the cause." She spread her hands in a gesture of acceptance. "The expert opinion is that Tommy has a nervous twitch, and, with luck, he'll grow out of it."

Tommy didn't grow out of his twitch. As it had done up to the age of five, it grew with Tommy, and by the time he was a teenager it was extremely distinct, seizing him every few seconds. Naturally, it was impossible for Tommy to take part in sports. And, of course, it made him afraid of the opposite sex. He avoided them completely.

When he was eighteen he visited his cousin, Charles, in a neighbouring city. Charles was a short-sighted youth with a frail physique. Perhaps because he, too, was not socially accepted, he and Tommy had always felt a bond of friendship. Charles lived life vicariously—in the romance and excitement of novels. But Tommy did not have patience for reading and was outgoing in spite of his handicap.

One evening they sat in Charles's den, talking about their futures, an ill-assorted pair—Charles's eyes pin-points behind his thick lenses as he peered towards his friend, who was talking enthusiastically and waving his arms, oblivious to the spasms which racked his body.

"You're lucky, Charlie," he was saying. "You know what you're going to do with your life. You live books. You'll be a librarian."

"That's right," said Charles.

"It'll suit you. I can see you now, running a huge library and sorting the new editions. But me?" Tommy gave a snort of derision. "What am I good for?"

"Come on now, Tommy," said Charles, "everybody can do something and you're no exception."

"All right then, what?" said Tommy. "I'm not a book person, and I'm not a scholar."

"You're a good talker," said Charles. "Maybe you could be a salesman."

Tommy looked dubious. "D'you really think so?"

"You're not worried about the twitch, are you?" said Charles callously. For years, they had both referred to Tommy's ailment as 'the twitch' as though it were an unpleasant third person who was always present. Charles knew that Tommy hated signs of pity so he added steel to his voice whenever he referred to it.

"I suppose I am," said Tommy.

"Well, don't be. I'm not suggesting that you go from door to door, frightening housewives to death!"

They both laughed at the macabre thought.

"But I do think you'd make a great salesman, if you sold things to men. You know what girls are like."

"The fewer of them the better," said Tommy, with deep feeling.

Tommy and Charles became adults without any abnormal developments. Charles completed his studies and became a librarian. Tommy tried a variety of jobs, eventually finding his niche as a car salesman. He seemed to enjoy the tough, masculine ambience.

Charles married a girl he met at the library. They bought a house and had a small family. Tommy would visit them once or twice a year.

Tommy's life soon developed a pattern. At work he was popular and fairly successful. Men liked him. He pleasantly mocked himself and he had a quick sense of humour.

His colleagues would often meet after work for some hard drinking. But by early evening Tommy would be alone in his bachelor apartment. He never went to the cinema or the theatre. He shunned social occasions where there were likely to be a preponderance of women, and the only strangers he met were possible purchasers who strolled into the firm's show-rooms.

As Tommy grew older, he found it increasingly difficult to maintain a cheerful façade. His sales figures declined and he moved from one job to another.

One winter's day Tommy collected his pay cheque. There was an ominous letter included. He was fired. The letter said 'retrenched' because of the 'current economic climate'. But he knew he had been dismissed because he couldn't sell his quota.

Tommy went home and locked the door. He took off his overcoat, went to his liquor cabinet, chose a bottle of rough brandy and poured himself a large drink. He knew he had been drinking too much lately. But what did it matter? Did anything matter? He drank slowly, steadily, with the despair of a man without hope.

What am I? he thought. A half man. When I'm in the street children point and teenage girls giggle and hide their faces. Even my friends think I'm a joke. They think I don't know the cheap laughs they get at my expense. He had overheard Sandy Jackson talking to one of the office girls.

"I like old Tommy," he'd said, "but you must admit he's

a bit of a jerk." Bit of a jerk! What a scream. Suddenly, perversely, Tommy wanted to see himself in a mirror and study his notorious twitch. But he kept no mirrors in the apartment, only a tiny shaving one. He poured more brandy and reached for a cigarette. A new pocket calendar he'd been given fell on to the table. He saw that his birthday fell on the next Tuesday.

I'll be fifty, he thought. His hand froze in mid-air holding the bottle. Slowly he put it down. Fifty years old! And what have I to show? No wife, no kids, no real home, no friend—no that wasn't true, Charles *was* a good friend. He was getting drunk and emotional, he had better be careful ...

But the knowledge remained with him that now, on the verge of fifty, he was more alone and miserable than at any other time in his life. His sense of isolation became almost physical. He needed to talk to someone. Impulsively he reached for the phone and dialled long-distance. He would talk to Charles. Perhaps it was too late. He looked at his watch. It was only 8 p.m. My God, he thought, I'm losing my grip, I thought it was past midnight, I've been drinking since I came home. The phone buzzed and he heard Charles's familiar voice. "Hello ..."

Tommy was so relieved to be in contact with his friend that he could hardly speak. "Hello, hello ... Who's there?" He heard Charles. He realised that if he didn't say something Charles would hang up.

"It's me," he shouted. "It's me, Charlie!"

"Hello, Tommy, speak of the devil!" He heard the pleasure in his friend's voice and felt warmed. "We've been wondering what you've been up to."

Hearing Charles's casual friendliness, Tommy was unexpectedly tongue-tied. There was so much to say, but where did one begin?

"Is anything wrong?" Urgency entered Charles's tone.

"I! ... I'm feeling ... well, depressed," said Tommy.

"You need a change of air," said Charles. "Why don't you come and stay with us. It's a long weekend and you're overdue for a visit!"

Tommy left immediately. He was met by Charles at the airport. In the car Charles produced a magazine and thrust it into Tommy's hands. "Read that! I've marked the page."

"What's it about?" asked Tommy.

"It says that hypnotism can, in some cases, cure nervous mannerisms. It's worth investigating."

Tommy opened the magazine and read the article which would change his life.

CLINICAL DIAGNOSIS

Two days after his fiftieth birthday, Tommy Twiller arrived at my clinic. Charles had already explained Tommy's problem, but it was only as Tommy sat opposite me that I realised the extent of his disability.

The word twitch was inadequate. With Tommy it was a convulsion. It began as a quiver of the head and escalated to a shake, accompanied by a variety of facial tics which contorted his face. These were followed by a pronounced movement of the shoulders and a jerk of the left arm.

The bizarre performance was repeated at intervals of approximately fifteen seconds.

Tommy Twiller was slightly above medium height, with greying hair. He was clean shaven, and had regular features. If it were not for the convulsions he would have been a handsome middle-aged man.

During our talks, I could find no clue as to the origin of Tommy's twitch. He said: "I've always had it. I cannot remember ever being without it, and my parents both told me that I grew up with a twitch."

I refused to accept this. Tommy had been subjected to a thorough physical examination. There was nothing wrong with his nervous system. A spasm of this magnitude had to have some origin.

In order to assess Tommy's personality I gave him a picture association test during one of our discussions. I handed him some magazines and asked him to page through them and describe to me the pictures he saw.

He did this efficiently for page after page, looking at the editorial content and the advertisements. At one point he said he felt absurd, having to describe the obvious, but I assured him that it was necessary and useful. Eventually Tommy came across an advertisement for Sloan's Liniment. This advertisement is familiar to readers in all parts of the world. It features the face of a dignified Victorian gentleman with a heavy, flowing moustache.

Tommy described the advertisement in perfect detail—except for the moustache. To him, the moustache was invisible. After a while, I asked him to describe the picture once more.

Again he did not mention the feature which dominated the picture. I thought this intriguing. I have always found that what people refuse to see is far more revealing than what they choose to see. Show a picture of a cowboy with guns to a violent person and he is likely to overlook the guns when describing it. He has a subconscious guilt about his violence so he unwittingly tries to hide it.

Tommy's case was made more mysterious by his complete lack of recollection concerning the moustache. He consciously knew of no one he had encountered in his lifetime with such a facial adornment. He was certain that his father had never worn a moustache at any time.

I asked if he could remember his grandparents. He replied that one grandfather had died before he was born. He could remember his other grandfather, but he was definitely clean shaven.

So far we had drawn a blank. And yet Tommy had produced no real evidence to confirm that one of his grandfathers had actually died before he was born. I suspected that this mysterious, missing Grandpa might prove crucial in the process of detection.

Hypnotism is a useful tool of psychology and this was clearly a case in which its use was called for. In a bid to uncover the identity of the man with the moustache I hypnotised Tommy. When he was in an appropriately deep state of hypnosis I asked him who the man with the moustache was. Tommy showed signs of distress. He was uncomfortable and unhappy, but he did not know of any man with a moustache.

I decided to regress Tommy. Under deep hypnosis it is possible to take a subject back, year by year, to earliest childhood, to the moment of emergence from the womb or even to the foetal state.

It is astonishing how mature adults revert to the physical attitudes, mannerisms and speech of an earlier age. I regressed Tommy to the age of ten and asked him where the forgotten Grandpa was. He did not know. He had no recollection of this Grandpa. I took him to the age of seven, six, five, then four ... Tommy Twiller, aged fifty, was now speaking with the hesitations and verbal fumblings of a four-year-old child.

The timbre of his voice changed. He *was* four. But still he had no knowledge of that Grandpa.

I tried once more. I regressed Tommy to the age of three.

"Where's your Grandpa?" I asked.

"Grandpa's dead," he said.

"When did he die?" I asked. At last, it seemed, we had struck oil.

"Yesterday," said the little boy's voice.

I regressed Tommy another day—to 'yesterday'.

"Now Tommy," I said, "Tell me exactly what happened today."

"I was in my room," said the little boy. "Playing with my toys."

"What happened then?"

"Grandpa came in."

"What did Grandpa look like?"

"Like Grandpa, of course!" The logic of a three-year-old.

"What happened next?"

The child was clearly becoming agitated. "Grandpa fell on top of me and I couldn't get up!"

Tommy began to shriek hysterically, re-living that horrifying moment and struggling to free himself.

"Now Tommy," I said, "I'm going to wake you. When

you are awake you will remember everything clearly and in detail, as you have been telling it to me now."

I then awakened him. Tommy, now fifty again, was still sobbing hysterically. The memory suppressed for so long had been brought from his subconscious mind to his conscious mind. Between sobs, he told me the whole story.

Tommy had been playing with his toys, a cheerful, normal child of three. His grandfather entered the room, no doubt intending to pat the child on the head and watch him at play. The elderly gentleman bent down, suffered a heart attack, and collapsed on the three-year-old. He was a heavily built man, with a handlebar moustache of the type then fashionable.

Tommy was trapped under his Grandpa. Grandpa's bristly moustache was pushed into Tommy's face, tickling him. The child struggled and screamed hysterically but was unable to escape. It was many minutes before servants heard his panic-stricken screaming and freed him.

The youngster's traumatic experience did not end there, however. Both Tommy's parents were away from the house at the time of the incident and possibly did not appreciate the severe impact of the tragedy on their son's sensibilities.

Tommy's grandfather was given a solemn funeral. His body was laid out and members of the family from all parts of the country gathered to pay their respects. Tommy, his hand in his father's, joined the procession as it filed past the bier.

As they walked slowly to the corpse, Tommy began to balk, but his father held his hand firmly. There was no escape. They came to the body and Tommy could see the waxen skin of his Grandpa, the bushy moustache boldly outlined against the deathly pallor of the face.

"Kiss your dear Grandpa goodbye. He has gone to Eternity," said Tommy's father.

"No! No!" the child shrieked.

"Kiss him," he commanded, and held Tommy's face so that the dead man's lips were close to his and Tommy could again feel the touch of the moustache. The child kissed the corpse and began to cry. The youngster's tears were not thought strange in such a setting and the family procession of mourning resumed.

The insensitive insistence that Tommy 'do his duty' to his grandfather when seen in the context of his terrifying encounter with death only a few days previously, created a psychic scar which crippled the child for forty-seven years.

The two horrifying incidents were too frightening for little Tommy to retain in his memory. At night he would restlessly re-enact the scenes. The terror evoked was too intense and overpowering for his three-year-old mind.

He created an escape. He blotted out all recollection. If he couldn't remember—he couldn't be frightened. Within days Tommy had completely forgotten his grandfather's existence and his death. Unfortunately, the brain's 'self-defence' mechanisms also have their failings.

When something is too horrible to be remembered and is suppressed by forcible loss of memory it practically invariably leaves a scar, an inhibition that can project itself later in any one of a thousand ways. In Tommy's case, it was 'The Twitch'.

Tommy was fortunate to recall the incident in full and harrowing detail while under hypnosis. Reacting to my suggestion, while under hypnosis, that he would still remember the details when conscious, he 'emotionalised' the incident and cleansed himself of it.

It is not sufficient to experience a purely intellectual awareness to achieve a cure. An abstract appreciation of the facts involved—the grandfather dropping dead and trapping the scared child and the subsequent encounter with the corpse during which he was compelled to kiss it—would not in itself remove the manifestation of the damage caused—the twitch.

But by travelling back on the stream of his subconscious memory (which forgets nothing) Tommy re-lived the experience and his mind was unable to blank out the searing memories again.

Tommy, fully conscious, registered the heartbreak and fear of those incidents from the past. He wept real tears,

139

and felt genuine anguish. By doing so, he cauterised the mental wound.

From that moment, we achieved our miracle. Tommy's twitch disappeared, never to return.

7: Look What I'm Doing

Nora Hughes carried the tub of washing up the back stairs into the kitchen and put it on the table. She stretched, and rubbed the small of her back in an effort to ease the ache.

She caught a glimpse of herself in the glass of the kitchen dresser. Her hair was unkempt and there was a smudge on her cheek. She realised it was the first time she'd inspected her appearance since breakfast time. It was now 3 p.m. She'd done nothing all day but cook breakfast, clean up after Jack left for work, prepare lunch for when he returned at 1 p.m. (the factory was near enough for him to come home for lunch), clean up again, and do the washing.

Not to mention chasing after Errol. Her four-year-old son was constantly in some sort of mischief. This morning he had taken a pair of shears from the garden shed and had damaged the neighbours' gates with the steel blades. She'd given him a thrashing but it didn't help.

Nora tried to tidy her hair but abandoned the attempt. What was the use, she thought. Within a few minutes it would be dishevelled again. She looked at the clock. Ten past three. She'd better get the supper ready. Jack was working overtime. He liked things to be right. He'd be home by 5.30, eat at 5.45, and be gone again by 6.15. By the time he finally came home, Nora would be asleep. For the next few weeks she would only see him briefly for meals. Even then the atmosphere was usually unpleasant. Jack was surly at the best of times. When he was working hard, as he was now, he was always irritable.

She heard the scream of a child and the sound knifed through her. Errol, again. She'd kill the little beast! Nora ran outside to see what was wrong. Errol's features were contorted in pain. He'd been riding the tricycle belonging to the boy next door. The boy tried to take it from him and in the tug-of-war Errol had fallen and bumped his knee.

"Serves you right!" said Nora. She grabbed him bodily off the ground by his hand and swung him inside the front gate.

"Go inside and stay there," she commanded.

Crying, he went inside. Nora went back to her chores and began the ironing. Later, she began to prepare the supper. Suddenly she thought: Where's Errol? He must be up to something. He's too quiet.

She found Errol in the lounge. He had opened the big salt container and he was busily pouring salt over the carpet, making patterns of white.

Nora clipped his face with her flat hand and he fell over backwards.

"You little horror," she cried. "Can't you do anything right?"

The boy clutched his face and looked at her wide-eyed. He began to cry. She took him by the shoulders and pushed him into the back yard. There was no damage he could do there.

When she went into the kitchen she smelt burning. She took the lid off one of the pots. The cauliflower was ruined. Nora felt tears of rage and frustration. Jack came home and complained about the burned cauliflower.

"You're lazy," he said, "you sit on your backside all day while I'm working and you don't even make a man a decent meal."

Nora let her resentment explode.

"Is that so?" she said. "Well, if you earned a decent wage I wouldn't have to scrimp and I'd have time to cook instead of doing every damned thing."

"Anyone could make this place tidy in an hour. You sit around all day watching the telly," he said, not even deigning to look at his wife.

"Who has to look after the bloody kid all day?" cried Nora. "And who has to do the washing? And the ironing? And buy the grub with the pennies you give me?"

Nora stood, her face white with anger. Errol, at the table, looked at his mother with alarm.

"Shut up and sit down," said Jack, shovelling food into his mouth.

"I will *not* shut up, for you or anyone else! I'm sick and tired of running around like a bloody slave! What thanks do I get? You haven't been near me for months. You've probably got some slut you do your so-called overtime with."

Jack Hughes deliberately put down his knife and fork He wiped his mouth with the back of his hand, and stood. Nora watched him, alarmed. She knew she'd gone too far.

Jack walked to her, not hurrying, and hit her twice, once in her ribs and once in the muscle of her shoulder. He punched so that the bruises didn't show. The force of the blows sent her reeling. She looked at her husband with hatred.

Jack Hughes put on his jacket and went to work. He didn't look back.

After he'd gone, Nora allowed herself the luxury of tears. When she had stopped crying she knew what to do. She took everything she valued ... not that there was much ... and packed her bags. Errol, still at the table, could see into the bedroom and he watched his mother's feverish packing.

"Where are you going, Mummy?" he asked, eventually.

"Away!" She said fiercely. "Away from you and your bloody father." She paused and looked around her ... "And away from this dump!"

She took her bags and walked to the front door. She'd been wanting to leave for months. She felt calm now that she had finally made up her mind. She took a final look at the place she'd called home for two years. If she never saw it again, it would be too soon. She looked at her son. He's the image of his father, she thought sourly. Let Jack look after him. They deserve each other. With a decisive gesture she went through the door and slammed it behind her.

143

Inside, sitting at the table, Errol screamed. "Mummy! ... Mummy!" He slipped from the chair and ran to the door.

He couldn't open the door and his mother couldn't hear him ... She didn't want to.

David Loft stopped talking to his wife because his daughter, Annie, had just ordered him to pay attention.

He and Susan were next to each other on the couch, and Annie, aged five, had brought her dolls and was about to give them a show.

"Look at me, Daddy," said Annie, her blue eyes framed by the blonde pigtails which reached below her shoulders. When she had both her parents' attention she grinned in triumph and invented conversations between the dolls, holding one in each hand.

After a while David interrupted the show to scoop his daughter up and kiss her.

"Daddy's got to go now, darling," he said.

"What time is the train, Dave?" asked Susan.

"I've got twenty minutes," he said.

"I'll run you to the station."

"Can I come too?" said Annie.

The three of them drove to the station. The train was on time. Annie and her mother waved goodbye.

At ten o'clock that night the phone next to Susan's bed rang. It awakened Annie, who was asleep next to her mother.

"Yes," said Susan.

"This is the police," said the voice.

The blood drained from Susan's face as she listened. Her husband had been mugged and had tried to resist. He had been stabbed and had died instantly.

After she'd put the phone down Susan didn't know what to do. Everything seemed unreal. Annie started pushing her, trying to evoke a response.

"Who was it, Mummy? Was it Daddy? Is he coming home?"

144

Susan collapsed on the bed as the horrible reality came home to her.

"He's never coming home again," she said. "He's dead."

Annie sat on the bed watching her mother's grief. Never seeing her father again was too awful to accept. She started to cry as well, out of sympathy more than comprehension.

When Errol Hughes's mother walked out on her husband and child, Errol's father decided he could not cope with a young boy. He placed him in the care of his sister, a married woman with three children of her own ... all of them older than Errol.

One day, after he had become accustomed to the routine of his new home, Errol was playing with his cousins, when another new arrival in the neighbourhood, a girl of ten, came walking past.

They began talking and the oldest of the boys pushed Errol forward to introduce him. He was an oddity, to be shown off.

"This is Errol," said the boy. "He hasn't got a mother."

The girl was fascinated. "Why not?" she asked.

"I don't know," said the boy. "She just ran away."

One of the younger boys said: "She didn't like him, otherwise she wouldn't have run away."

Errol stood stiff and quiet, his eyes moving from one face to another as they spoke.

"Never mind, Errol," said the girl compassionately. "Perhaps she'll come back some day."

When Annie Loft was thirteen, a lodger came to live with them. Susan Loft had not re-married, and it was a struggle for her to support herself and the young girl. The arrival of Larry Evans seemed a godsend. The money he paid for his accommodation made all the difference to her budget.

Larry Evans was a trombonist and a good one. He played for studio sessions which paid handsomely. He enjoyed the homely atmosphere of Annie's house, and he stayed on. Evans was a man of forty, gentle with humorous eyes. He'd been living on the coast, but, recently divorced, he had moved to sever his connections with the past. Larry and Annie soon became very close. She loved music. Larry encouraged her interest and persuaded Susan to send her to a dancing school.

Annie already had the beginnings of a fine figure coupled with the face of a beautiful innocent. When Larry had been living with them for three months, Susan went to visit her parents for a long weekend. Annie was appearing in an amateur concert on the Saturday so it was arranged that she would stay behind. Larry took her to the concert. She danced well and took her bows with confidence.

As Larry drove her home he felt her hand slide into his. He was not surprised ... Annie was affectionate and sought warmth whenever she could. He had to free his hand to change gears. He glanced at Annie and saw her frown. After that she sat silently, ignoring him. Larry grinned at her childish pique.

When they reached home he fussed over Annie, fetching a drink for her and a beer for himself from the refrigerator. Larry relaxed with a copy of *Downbeat*. Annie sat beside him, peering over his shoulder. He held the magazine at an angle so that she could read it with him and she snuggled against his shoulder. Larry looked surprised and she gave him a grin. Annie had lovely eyes, but their most notable characteristic was an expression of trusting innocence. Now, as she curled against him, Larry found her expression affecting.

Impulsively, he kissed her lightly on the cheek. As he did so he felt her hand cup the back of his neck and pull him closer. Her lips found his and he began kissing her. He broke away as he realised what he was doing.

"Hey," he said, defensively. "Don't get carried away."

"I like kissing you," she said. "Your moustache tickles." She came to him again and kissed him. He put his arms around her and felt her breast. She moved to make herself more accessible. Although aroused Larry pushed Annie away.

"For God's sake," he said, his voice shaking. "What are

146

you doing to me?" He took another beer. Annie lay quietly, smiling at him.

"What are you afraid of?" she asked. He looked at her, blonde and sweet-faced, her long brown legs draped across the couch.

What indeed? He pulled himself together. She's only thirteen years old!

"Cut it out, Annie," he said, forcing disapproval into his voice. "You're only a child."

"I thought you liked me," said Annie, her lower lip trembling.

"Of course I like you," said Larry. "But *like* is one thing and love is another." He picked up his magazine. "I'm going to bed," he said, 'it's about time you did, as well."

He bent, kissed her on the forehead and walked off, before she could kiss him back. It's ridiculous, thought Larry as he prepared for bed. Here I am, a man of forty with two kids, running away from a thirteen-year-old. But what do you do when someone that age makes a play for you? Being honest he had to admit that he'd like nothing better than a session in bed with such a beautiful nymphet.

He lay on the bed, wearing only his trunks, and concentrated on his beer and his *Downbeat*.

Ten minutes later there was a tap on his door.

"Larry," he heard Annie's voice.

"Yes, what is it?"

Annie pushed open the door. She was wearing a wrap, and held it closed with one hand at her neck. She sat on his bed. Her hair was drawn back and she looked exquisitely young, fresh and innocent.

"The concert next week," she said. "Won't you take me to it?"

"Sure," he said. "I told you I would."

"Thanks," said Annie. "I don't know what I'd do without you. You're my only real friend."

She took his hand in hers and released the wrap. It fell open revealing her breasts. They were still not fully formed.

147

He forced himself to lift his gaze from her body to her eyes. She looked angelic ... sex with innocence. She took his hand, placed it against her breast, then looked at his hand.

It was a curiously childish gesture and it flashed through Larry's mind that this was probably the first time a male hand had ever touched this young breast. The thought moved him to tenderness and he pulled the girl closer. Her lips were toothpaste fresh on his mouth. Annie turned to him and the wrap fell away completely.

She took off Larry's trunks and with a child-like delight began to investigate his body. Annie was utterly selfless. Her only concern was for him. Afterwards, she fell asleep in his arms like a small child.

When Susan came back from her holiday, she found a note from Larry saying that he had decided to live with a bachelor friend in town. Although Larry moved to assuage his conscience, he continued to see Annie and they often made love. He found she was ready to, at any time, day or night.

This was brought home to him when he arrived at his new apartment one evening. He walked into the lounge and stopped. His flat-mate, Arthur, was with Annie on the carpet. Though she was in the middle of the sexual act she lifted a hand to him and grinned.

Larry coughed, poured himself a stiff drink and went into his bedroom. He sat on his bed and thought: I'm jealous. That little girl just gives herself away like a present. A few minutes later there was a rap on his door and Annie came in. She was unabashed and as friendly and affectionate as ever.

To Arthur's surprise, Annie stayed in Larry's bed that night. He asked her about her encounter with Arthur. She dismissed the incident lightly. "He got carried away so I let him do it." She giggled and kissed his chest. "He's only a boy. You're a man."

A few weeks later, Annie stopped coming to the apartment. She drifted into the arms of other men, multitudes of them.

When Errol Hughes was twenty-two he married a woman much older than himself. She had money and had travelled. Errol had found stage management work in television and he met his prospective bride on an assignment.

Nanette was a handsome woman of thirty-five and experienced sexually. She introduced Errol to subtleties which he had not known in his occasional encounters with the opposite sex. He developed a compulsion to marry Nanette. At first she laughed, saying that marriages between young men and older women never lasted.

But he persisted. She was flattered and though she believed they would only enjoy married life for a short while, she finally consented. The marriage lasted three years, during which Errol's ardour soon cooled. As she had married him in order to have a vigorous young lover, Nanette quickly arranged the divorce. Errol accepted the decision philosophically. He had developed a penchant for bizarre sex during his travels with the television team and he looked forward to the freedom of bachelordom once again.

The paths of Errol Hughes and Annie Loft crossed when he was fifty and she was twenty-two. Errol was now a senior television crew manager and his work had taken him around the world. He had never married again, and had now decided that marriage was not for him.

Annie was a successful dancer and had recently taken singing lessons. Her agent had told her that a girl with her looks didn't need an outstanding voice to get by in cabaret.

"We'll work out an act," he said, "dancing, singing, a few point numbers, clever patter, and you'll be earning twice the money."

To the agent's disappointment, Annie proved to be stiff and unnatural in cabaret. She lacked the quality of confidence. Although she had some success in minor clubs it became obvious she would never graduate to the big time. On New Year's Day there was a show-business party at the television studio.

Errol spotted Annie on the other side of the room. She was stunningly beautiful. Her looks were made immeasurably more appealing by the sweetness of her expression. He

149

was standing with a director who had used Annie once in a short feature.

"She photographs well," he said. "But she freezes up on camera. Pity!" He gave Errol an amused look. "She's a raver, if you're interested."

"She's a knock-out," said Errol. The director took Errol over to Annie and introduced them.

Errol found himself talking more than he normally did, drawn out by Annie's attentiveness and laughter. She seemed to hang on to every word he said. He was flattered by her and entranced by her looks.

Errol asked if she'd like a lift home and to his surprise, she accepted. Errol was not particularly good-looking and he had never been over-successful with women. Annie was so outstanding that he expected her to be booked with dates for weeks to come. When he realised she had no arrangement for later that evening, he was delighted.

As he drove, he answered her questions about his work. It seemed no time before they were outside her apartment.

"Well, it's been a pleasure . . ." His words tailed off.

Annie had drawn her skirt up and slipped out of her panties, he could see her pubic hair. She was watching him with a half smile.

This totally unexpected gesture of sexual abandonment shocked Errol but he was extremely aroused erotically. He reached for her and took her across the front seat of the car. They were both oblivious to the danger of being seen by passers-by.

It was not only sexually that Annie and Errol got on well together. Annie was a good listener, and Errol was an outgoing talker. Annie liked his maturity and Errol was flattered by being seen with such a beautiful girl. Annie moved into Errol's flat and after three months they decided to get married. They had a quiet wedding with a party afterwards.

They both enjoyed talking about sex, as well as actively taking part in it. They read sexy books together, and enjoyed pornography. They once bought a manual which described a hundred different positions and they tried to re-enact them. Annie had willingly co-operated.

But for some reason her enthusiasm for oral sex quickly diminished. Errol, who enjoyed the feeling of masculine superiority associated with this sexual activity was visibly upset. Annie didn't give a point-blank refusal, but always diverted his attention with some other sexual ploy which he didn't find as satisfying.

On their wedding night, Errol was determined to persuade Annie to perform as she had done when they first met. They began to play sexual charades.

One of Annie's favourite games was to pretend that Errol was her Daddy. Errol would slowly undress her and put her to bed. Then they would make love. When they were alone, Annie presented herself, fully dressed. Errol undressed her, taking his time until she was nude. Then he picked her up, placed her on the bed and made love to her. It was tender and satisfying.

An hour later Annie wanted sex again. Errol placed his hands on her shoulders to guide her head between his legs.

Annie flushed and shook her head.

"You mean you won't?" he said.

"I don't want to," she said curtly.

"I don't understand you," said Errol. "You're game for anything, yet you refuse me the one thing I want."

"Please don't go on about it," said Annie. "I won't do it, and that's all."

"But it doesn't make sense. You know I'll do any damned thing *you* want, but I expect you to do the same for me!"

"Well I can't," said Annie.

Frustrated by her stubbornness, Errol threw his glass against the wall in anger. "Bloody logic," he muttered to himself.

At once Annie came to him, kissing him and caressing him, genuinely concerned that he was so upset. She led him to the bed, aroused him and made love to him. But

151

she flatly refused to engage in fellatio and when Errol finally fell asleep he was still frustrated.

Apart from this one note of dissonance, their marriage was harmonious for the first few weeks. They liked each other's friends and their careers were complementary to each other. Errol was able to arrange a television spot for her, and her agent became more optimistic about cabaret engagements.

After they had been married for six months, Errol was floor-managing a live television show which he expected would keep him occupied until after midnight. But the programme was cancelled due to the sudden illness of a politician and Errol arrived home at 10 p.m. He unlocked the door, walked into the living-room and almost stumbled over Annie, indulging in fellatio with a man Errol had never seen before.

Errol lost his temper. Berserk, he kicked the man in the ribs and sent him sprawling. Annie ran screaming into the bedroom and locked it. Errol began to demolish the furniture in the living room, giving cries of rage as he shattered chairs and hurled china ornaments against the walls. The stranger quickly dressed and ran through the front door, unnoticed by Errol engaged in destruction.

Finally, Errol collapsed on the carpet, weeping. Slowly the bedroom door opened and Annie appeared. She took Errol's head in her hands and stroked his forehead. She sadly bent over her distraught husband and comforted him. Paradoxically, Errol catching his wife in sexual betrayal brought them closer together.

"I should have realised from the beginning," he said later that night, when he had recovered sufficiently to talk to Annie.

He lit a cigarette and inhaled. Annie sat on the edge of the bed, demure and beautiful, listening attentively.

"You're a nymphomaniac," he said. "I should have known. No normal woman is as sexy as you. The way you took your pants off in the car ..." He shook his head, remembering.

"Who was that fellow with you tonight anyway?" he asked.

"John somebody-or-other. I met him at a rehearsal."

"How can you explain that you did with him, a complete stranger, what you won't do with me, your husband?" Anger was re-entering Errol's voice.

"Please darling, I can't explain it. Don't nag me." She walked up and down, her hands fluttering nervously.

It was the first time Errol had seen her upset. The sight of her discomposure moved him.

"Well," he said, "we'll come to terms with it." He put his arms around her and held her closely.

She snuggled to him. To his amazement she immediately became sexually aroused. She kissed his mouth and darted her tongue between his lips.

Still drained by the shock of discovering Annie with another man, the last thing Errol wanted was sex. He pushed Annie away from him violently.

"You're the bloody limit," he said savagely. He walked from the bedroom and slammed the door. "I'm going to bed . . . on my own."

As the weeks passed, Errol became obsessed with the image of his wife and the man on the living-room floor. His reactions had been curiously mixed. What he had seen had shocked him, but the sight of his wife bent in a supplicant attitude over another man, he had found exciting. Within the next month, Errol caught his wife on two more occasions . . . both times in their own home.

First, he came home in mid-afternoon to find Annie kissing a television journalist on the couch. The journalist looked discomforted and left, mumbling apologies. Annie just sat there, her eyes as innocent as ever. Errol was utterly bewildered. In frustration and confusion he struck Annie with his fist. The force of the blow toppled her from the couch on to the floor. She looked at him with silent reproach. Errol stayed the night with a friend.

The second time, to Errol's astonishment, was at nine o'clock in the morning. He left the house early then discovered he had forgotten a document. He returned to find Annie with the laundryman. Errol was tormented by knowing that in both cases if he had arrived a few minutes later he would have seen his wife having sexual intercourse.

He was haunted by his regret that he had been too early. He *wanted* to see Annie having sex with other men. He particularly wanted to see her having oral sex, because it was denied to him.

He decided on a plan. Dan Miller, who first introduced him to Annie, was just the person to use. Errol knew that Dan went to sex parties where group sex was common practice. He invited Dan for dinner one evening. Annie wasn't a good cook but she arranged to have a dinner sent in and Errol made sure there was plenty to drink. By the time the meal was over, they were all in a good mood. Annie cleared the table and went into the kitchen. She was wearing a tight fitting cat-suit and Errol saw that Dan was watching her figure at every opportunity.

"She looks sexy, eh, Dan?" he said.

Dan was surprised by the question.

"Beautiful," he answered, non-committally.

"You must have 'had' her, seeing you met her before me," said Errol, careful not to sound jealous.

Dan was puzzled. The last thing he wanted was an outburst of belated jealousy.

"Don't misunderstand me," said Errol. "I'm not making a scene. We both know Annie. She digs sex with almost anyone. I don't mind."

Dan relaxed. This was the sort of situation he liked.

"It's great to have no hang-ups," he said. "It means there's no limit to the kicks you can get out of sex."

Errol was delighted by his response.

Dan continued: "To be honest, nothing ever happened with Annie. I fancied her ... who wouldn't? ... but there wasn't a spare minute at the time that I knew her."

Errol said softly: "Do you still fancy her?"

Dan's eyes narrowed. "Of course."

"Then you can have her," said Errol.

Now Dan understood the situation.

"I suppose you want to watch us, eh?"

Errol nodded. "Have another drink," he said. Errol poured a generous measure. Annie returned from the kitchen and he gave her a drink as well.

For the next hour Errol manipulated the conversation. At every opportunity he slipped in salacious remarks. He knew that Annie responded to verbal titillation. Eventually, they were all affected by the liquor. Annie's eyes were shiny and Dan was being more than attentive to her.

"Annie," said Errol, his voice thick with drink. "Dan fancies you."

Annie looked from her husband to Dan.

"I said you wouldn't mind."

Annie looked back to Errol, her expression clouded.

"You mean you want us to make love."

"That's right," Errol said, watching Annie intently for signs of resistance. "I want you to do it in front of me."

"All right," said Annie. "If you really want me to."

"More than anything," said Errol.

Dan pulled Annie from her chair and sat her on his lap. He kissed her and she responded instantly.

Errol sat, his emotions churning, watching their love-play.

They began to undress until they stood naked before him.

"Do it, Annie," shouted Errol hoarsely. He gestured, and she understood his meaning. Her face was expressionless but she did as she was told.

Dan lay back and Annie caressed him with her lips to a groaning climax. As he watched Annie with the naked man, Errol felt triumphant. His hands were moist and he felt elated and dizzy. Annie rose to her feet and stood unsmiling.

"I did what you wanted," she said.

"Yes," said Errol. "It was great."

"I'm going to bed now," said Annie. She turned and walked into the bedroom.

Dan casually picked up his clothes and dressed. Finally he sat down and finished his drink.

"You really surprised me tonight, Errol," he said approvingly. "I always felt you were a bit square, but not after tonight. We must do it again."

"Any time, Dan," said Errol eagerly. "Any time."

After Dan had gone, Errol sat thinking. He had been erotically stimulated by the sight of his wife with another man. But on a different level to the sex he had a feeling of exhilaration. It was as though something unpleasant within him had been removed. Errol knew that he must see that scene again. It didn't matter who the man was. It could be anyone as long as Annie degraded herself. Errol felt cheerful. He went into the bedroom. Annie was in bed, reading.

She put down the book. "Why did you make me do that?" she asked.

"Didn't you like doing it?"

"No!" said Annie petulantly.

"But why?" asked Errol. He sat on the bed next to his wife. "You always enjoy sex. If you'd been left alone with Dan you'd have ended up doing the same thing."

"It's different," said Annie sulkily. "I only did it because you wanted me to."

Errol was concerned that he might not be able to repeat the sensations of the evening.

"Look, Annie, all you ever think about is sex. You have sex like other people eat. You must realise that no one else would put up with it. But I will. All I ask is that you co-operate and have it sometimes while I watch."

Annie looked at him searchingly, her habitual expression of trust marred by bewilderment.

"All right, Errol," she said finally. "But only because you really want me to."

"Thanks," he said, and kissed her.

He got into bed and turned to go to sleep. He was drowsing when he felt Annie's exploratory hand.

He brushed the hand away. "Not now," he said. "I want to sleep."

Annie lay next to him racked by confusing thoughts and sexual desire. Just before she fell asleep, she thought: He spoiled it. Why did he have to do that?

156

After that night, Errol arranged threesomes whenever he could. Once the word got around that Errol and his beautiful wife were ravers there was no shortage of volunteers. Annie complied, but she was not happy about it. Yet, three or four times a week Errol would return home to find signs of men having been there. Each time, Errol would lose his temper, but invariably, they would have a tender reunion in bed.

But one day Errol thought of a variation. That night he brought home two friends, Dan and a colleague. Annie was out and arrived home at nine. Her lipstick was smudged and her hair was mussed. Errol felt anger but pushed it aside. This was not the time. He introduced Annie to Bill, Dan's friend, and explained:

"I thought we'd do something a little different tonight."

"How different?" said Annie defensively. She looked at Bill again. He was good-looking.

Errol explained that they would get undressed and that Annie would have sex with Dan and Bill together.

"What about you?" asked Annie with clinical curiosity.

"I'll look after myself," he said. Errol now increased his voyeuristic enjoyment by masturbating.

"I don't know," said Annie, but she soon agreed.

Errol sat in his chair and watched the trio perform. In the anti-climax that followed the sexual acrobatics, Errol caught a strange expression in Annie's eyes. He went to her, patted her, then kissed her on the forehead.

"You were very good tonight, darling," he said.

To his amazement and to the horror of the others, she burst into tears, ran into the bathroom and slammed the door behind her. Bill and Dan dressed, apologising that they had to rush off.

There was a scream from the bathroom. The three men stood, immobilised. Errol ran to the bathroom and wrenched the door open. Annie was sprawled across the bath. She had slashed her wrist with a razor blade. Blood was spurting in a red gush against the tiled wall.

Errol rushed into the living-room to ask the others for help. But the front door stood open and Errol could hear footsteps running down the street. With a towel he managed to staunch the flow of blood. Then he took a bandage and made a tourniquet.

Annie was admitted to hospital and visited by a psychiatrist who recommended regular treatment.

Errol was stunned. He had thought everyone had been enjoying themselves. He had no idea what had gone wrong, or why.

CLINICAL DIAGNOSIS

Annie and Errol represent two psychological disasters. Once I familiarised myself with Annie's background I asked her to bring her husband. In the course of many consultations we explored their pasts.

Annie, had a strong early relationship with her father. Then she lost him ... killed violently and meaninglessly. Annie then spent her life trying to find a substitute. She soon learned that the easiest way to gain affection and attention from men is sex.

The combination of a specific need and a strong psychological sex urge made her a classic example of nymphomania ... a girl lacking in confidence, using sex as a means to find a father. When Larry Evans, the forty-year-old musician, moved into the Loft household he was tailor-made for Annie. At the first opportunity she gave herself to him physically. This unwithholding attitude continued into her adult life. Her body was all she felt she had to give, and she gave it generously. Although she slept with young men, her preference was for men of maturity.

When she met Errol he seemed the sort of male she required. He was fifty, not good-looking but he responded to her blatant sexuality. This pleased her enormously. The marital bond confirmed to Annie that Errol was her father as well as her husband. Therefore, she could not accede to his request for oral sex. It is normal among women who seek 'fathers' to regard oral sex as an incestuous act. She could rationalise other sexual acts as being attempts to please her 'father-husband' ... to give him a 'treat'. Her need for re-assurance that Errol was her father, drove her to acts of infidelity so that he would discover her, chide her and forgive her.

This was the pattern which Errol unwittingly followed, displaying rage and sometimes violence, but always taking her back—precisely the reassurance she needed. Errol's own compulsions, however, exerted disastrous tensions on the relationship.

Annie, motivated by her all-important desire to please her 'father', agreed to his strange sexual requests. She had oral sex with another man in front of him. The act held no charm for her because of the circumstances. Her 'father' was sitting there, watching and giving tacit approval. This was not what Annie wanted. Her strategy of sexual infidelity was intended to evoke disapproval, proving that her 'father' loved her.

Therefore, when the voyeur 'scene' was introduced by Errol, Annie sought more sexual conquests to obtain further reassurance from her 'father'. The acts that Annie thought of as sexual betrayal, in front of Errol, created extreme tension within Annie. Her breaking point was when Errol escalated the level of betrayal by introducing yet another man. Then, he behaved in a paternal manner, patting her, kissing her on the forehead and telling her she had been good.

She could not overlook her 'father' approving of her being 'naughty' with other men. This meant one thing: her father did not love her. In her uncertainty and insecurity Annie attempted self-destruction.

Errol's background was complementary to Annie's. He had also lost a parent under traumatic circumstances. His mother, a cold, violent woman, walked out on him. The honesty mixed with cruelty of other children sharpened his pain. His playmates reminded him that his mother didn't love him. Errol hated his mother ... but he desperately wanted her.

When he was twenty-two he found a mother-figure ... Nanette, the woman who broadened his sexual experience.

As soon as they were married, the mother-concept became dominant and he preferred to fuss and pamper his wife rather than make physical love. This was aversion to having sex with his 'mother'. The marriage was a failure and Errol fell into a haphazard existence for many years.

When he met Annie he was fascinated by her appearance of virtue, which he associated with his idealised concept of motherhood. When Annie proved to be sexually brazen, he was swept into a complex nexus of sexual and psychological inter-action. He still retained the childish belief that his parents were incapable of making mistakes. His mother was right to desert him. He must be worthless, otherwise his mother would never have left him. At the same time, he hated his 'mother'. His psyche was still bleeding from his mother's savagery.

Two powerful emotions created Errol's neurotic need to watch his wife taking part in sexual acts with other men.

Seeing his wife being physically violated by other men gave him masochistic pleasure. It was hurtful to his pride, but because he was inferior (his rationalisation) it was right that he should be hurt. On the other hand—and in Errol's case this was more important of the two considerations—by having his mother-wife submit to the indignity of being used by two men, he was revenging himself. The sight of his 'mother' being debased, balanced the scales. We were not able to achieve a great deal with Annie and Errol. Annie improved her confidence. She learned to realise that she would not have been able to seduce so many men, if she were not remarkably attractive. This gain in confidence helped her considerably with her career. She also accepted that she was searching for a father-figure. This minimised her behaviour.

Errol proved resistant to treatment and no progress was made. Errol and Annie are still married. Their sex world is still aberrant, their lives generally unhappy. Their parents left them a legacy of chaos.

8: And Here is the News

Guy James woke up to the sound of a dog barking down the street. That must be Jeff's Alsatian, he thought drowsily. Suddenly he was wide awake. He looked at the clock. It was 7 a.m.

Guy, a seven-year-old, enjoyed being the first person awake in the house. It gave him the feeling of being special, as though he and the old house shared secrets. He dressed hurriedly and went quietly out of his room to the familiar sounds of early morning. It was a quiet suburban area and Guy knew all the boys in the neighbourhood and their pets.

Guy opened the front door. There were the milk-bottles, as usual, and the morning newspaper. Guy picked up the paper and was about to take it to his father. Tempted for a moment, he opened the paper at the comic section, then feeling guilty, folded the paper again.

Whistling out of tune he went to his parents' bedroom and knocked.

"Hey, Dad," he shouted. "It's seven o'clock."

He heard a groan, then his father's deep voice saying: "Come on in."

Guy bounded into the room, jumping headlong on to the bed next to his father, who was still rubbing his eyes.

"Hold on!" said his father, overwhelmed by Guy's exuberance. "Steady!" He took the newspaper and arranged his bedside table, moving his cigarettes, the glass with his dentures, and some magazines so that he could put down the folded newspaper. Peter James looked at his son. He was amused, as always, by Guy's vitality. The boy was full of energy, but it was easy to see through his childish guile.

"You want the comics, don't you?" asked Peter.

"Please, Daddy," said Guy.

His father glanced perfunctorily at the page of strip-cartoons and gave it to him. In her own bed, Ella James stirred and mumbled incomprehensibly.

"It's five past seven, Ella," said Peter. His wife slowly put on her dressing gown, went downstairs like a sleep-walker and made the morning tea.

She brought the tray upstairs. Mother, father and son drank tea and read the paper together.

Later, Peter went to work and Ella and Guy watched him drive away.

One day, when Guy was nine, he visited Fred, a young friend who lived nearby. At the back of Fred's house there was an enormous, dense hedge which they loved to explore. They were making a hide-away, breaking off the branches and twigs to form a cave, in which they could crouch and plot. The hedge was springy and tough. It was hard work using bare hands. They climbed the six-foot hedge and balanced on the top.

A wasp flew past them and returned, its buzz full of menace. Guy saw the colourful insect, jerked backwards to avoid it and lost his footing. As he fell backwards, he saw concern and helplessness on Fred's face, then he felt a stunning blow. He lay half-conscious on a pile of bricks. He wiped his mouth with his hand. He looked at his hand. It was covered with blood.

Fred's mother rushed him home and called the doctor.

"It's not serious, thank goodness," said the GP. "As far as I can see Guy has chipped a few teeth. He'll have a rather ragged smile from now on."

"As long as there's nothing to worry about," said his mother, relieved.

When Guy left school he had no doubts about the career he wanted. Television had always fascinated him and he was lucky enough to land a job on the news staff of the local television station. He was good at the job. He enjoyed the immediacy of the work, the bustle, pressure and being involved with important events.

One day the Station News Editor called for him. Bob Derby was an informal man, sometimes brusque to the point of rudeness, but liked by his staff.

"We've decided to move you up the ladder," said Derby, offering Guy a cigarette.

"That's great," said Guy, wondering what they had in mind.

"Somebody suggested that you'd make a news-reader," said Derby. "How old are you?"

"Twenty-six," said Guy.

"That's okay, then," said Derby. "You look an indeterminate age, and you have a good voice."

Guy was elated. He'd never thought he could ever be on camera. He had always considered himself as an anonymous writer.

"There's one thing, though," said Derby, looking at Guy.

"Oh. What's that?"

"Your teeth," grinned Derby. "You look like a ragged-tooth shark when you smile."

"Oh, that," said Guy, good-naturedly. "I fell on my face when I was a kid."

"I thought there was something odd about you," said the older man, and laughed. "But you'll have to have them fixed. We can't have you snarling into the camera like Dracula."

Guy said he'd see a dentist right away. There were many dentists who specialised in cosmetic work, so he made an appointment. Years before, the dentist who had treated Guy at the time of the accident had recommended that there was no need for dental work to be done at that time. He'd told Guy's father that if Guy became self-conscious about his teeth then it might be worth while to cap them. But it seemed an unnecessary expense.

Now, studying Guy's teeth, this dentist shook his head in perturbation.

"You haven't been looking after them," he said.

"Not really, I suppose," said Guy.

"Damaged teeth, as these are, are vulnerable to decay.

163

They're in bad shape. You say you must get them right because of your work?"

"Yes," said Guy. "Viewers expect news-readers to have regular teeth."

"Well," said the dentist. "They'll have to come out. If I patch them, fill them and cap them it'll be a long unpleasant procedure and I still couldn't guarantee the final result.

"Let me remove the uppers, which are most damaged, and cap the two bottom teeth. We can give you dentures, these days, which look better than real teeth."

Guy agreed. He returned the next day and the dentist removed the affected top teeth. It was painless and Guy was unruffled. Before the teeth were extracted the dentist asked Guy to bite on a wax-like substance so that he could take an impression for the false teeth.

After the teeth had been removed and the bleeding staunched, Guy had to repeat this procedure to give an impression of his gums. Sitting in the dentist's chair, Guy suffered considerable boredom, but no pain. When the dentist was satisfied with the mouth impressions, he promised Guy that the dentures would be ready in a week.

A week later Guy's false teeth were fitted. They slipped into place with precision. The nurse brought a mirror and he smiled into it. The dentist had done a first-class job. The teeth looked perfect, yet with a natural asymmetry. As Guy sat in the dentist's chair, admiring his new appearance, his face contorted and he retched violently. The new teeth fell to the floor at the nurse's feet.

Trying again and again, Guy could not retain the dentures in his mouth. His stomach and throat rejected the teeth repeatedly. The longest he could keep them in his mouth was a minute. After that, the energy-draining retching would begin.

"We have a problem," said the dentist.

"You're not kidding," said Guy. "I'm not going to be the first toothless news-reader. I've got to get these things to stay in my mouth!"

Guy James's aversion to dentures in his mouth is shared by many people. Some sufferers cannot masticate their food properly, using only their gums. In Guy's case it affected an important job opportunity.

When recommended to do so by his dentist, Guy first underwent a series of allergy tests to establish whether the revulsion was caused physically. The allergy tests proved negative. It seemed clear that Guy had developed a mental problem concerning artificial teeth.

Aversion to false teeth is such a common complaint that I was certain I knew the cause of Guy's problem. However I hypnotised him and regressed him to childhood to make sure. It was as I had thought.

Up to the age of eight, the James family—Peter James, Ella James and Guy—had enjoyed early morning tea and the reading of the newspaper together. Every day Guy would fetch the morning newspaper and bring it to his father. And every morning Guy would see his father's dentures in the glass next to the bed.

It was a stomach-turning sight. Discoloured teeth, covered in fragments of undigested food, floating in grease-filmed liquid. Young Guy felt nauseated each time he saw them. Then, many years later, when he was forced to put dentures into his *own* mouth, the disgust returned, subconsciously.

When Guy witnessed this unpleasant sight for the first time, he did not wish to associate it with his parents, who were images of perfection to him. Therefore he blocked out the image. If an image is so awful, in the first place, that it has to be blocked out, it is already a minor neurosis.

Years later, when Guy was an adult and he found himself in a similar situation, the memory of the repugnance came back—but more strongly than before. In this instance nothing could be achieved by directly informing Guy of the origin of his aversion, as there was no way of making him emotionalise it. Instead, we used the problem itself as the cure.

In a matter-of-fact manner I told Guy how, in the 'olden days', people who wore artificial teeth, put them in glasses of liquid overnight. *Anyone*, I said, would have been sick at the thought of having to put *those* old-fashioned, unhygienic teeth in their mouths.

But, I emphasised, modern artificial teeth were totally different. They were made of plastic and were thoroughly hygienic. It was even possible to sleep with *these* teeth still in the mouth. They need only be taken out occasionally for a light brushing with sterilising fluid.

I told Guy to place his new teeth in his mouth for only ten minutes at a time. Then we slowly increased the period until he was wearing them for an hour or more. I gave Guy detailed instructions on how to look after his teeth —and I instructed him *never* to keep them in a glass of water. It was a quick cure. Quite soon, Guy wore his teeth easily and without nausea.

It is human nature to accept change, and I have found it a good treatment policy to play on this aspect of the human mind. This is why I encouraged Guy to appreciate the advantages of scientific progress in dental mechanics.

A great number of people have problems concerning going to the dentist. Many of them stem from unpleasant experiences in childhood, when they went to the dentist for the first time. The techniques of dentistry have progressed remarkably, especially since the advent of the high-speed drill. People suffering from an aversion to dentistry should take cognisance of these improvements.

9: Double or Nothing

The phone rang and Jake went to answer it.

"Hello," he said.

"Is that Mr Marcus?"

"Speaking."

"This is John Thompson, from the *Record*. You remember you asked me if I could get you a ticket for the concert on Friday. Well, I managed. Shall I send it to you or would you like to collect it?"

"That's very thoughtful of you," said Jake into the phone, raising his voice in the hope that his wife would hear the conversation. "Ticket for the concert, eh? I've been looking forward to hearing Corelli. He's a master in his field."

"Oh?" The voice at the other end of the phone sounded bewildered.

"Would you send it to my house?" said Jake. "It's most kind of you. I don't know how to repay you."

"I'll send it, Mr Marcus. But you *do* remember the arrangement, don't you?" The voice's puzzlement was even more pronounced.

"Of course, of course. Thank you again," said Jake, and hung up.

He raised his voice and called through to his wife, who was in the bedroom, attending to their only son, Ronald, who was eight months old.

"Did you hear that, Sarah? That was the Editor of the *Record*. He's sending me a ticket for the concert on Friday."

He walked to the edge of the hall and looked into the bedroom. His young wife, Sarah, was changing a nappy. She didn't look up. Jake felt resentment toward the infant, squalling and kicking its legs. Damn kid, he thought. Everything had been marvellous until it arrived and disrupted the household. It had been an accident, too. It wasn't as though they'd planned to have him.

"Did you hear me, Sarah?" he asked.

"Of course, Jake," she said, looking at him affectionately. "That's marvellous."

Jake beamed with pleasure.

Sarah thought: If only Jake wouldn't always exaggerate! That wasn't the Editor of the *Record* on the phone. Jake hasn't even met him. He's always trying to prove he knows important people.

"Darling," she called. "Come and look at Ronald."

Jake moved to his wife's side and peered down at the squalling child. "Beautiful," he said, but it sounded false even to him. Sarah hadn't even heard him. She was cooing at the baby, powdering it and tickling its cheek.

Jake walked away and stood in the doorway, shoulders hunched. He was strongly built with brown eyes and dark hair. An impressive figure and a rising business man. Well known in the town. In his small way he cultivated musicians and entertainers. It gave him a feeling of vicarious importance.

He thought: It's early yet. I think I'll go and drop off the fifty pence at the *Record* for the chap who arranged the ticket. The truth was that Frank had forgotten all about the concert. By the time he remembered it was sold out. In desperation he had called an acquaintance on the newspaper. Journalists always seemed to be able to wangle seats. He'd offered him the money if he could pull it off, and he had.

"I think I'll go and see Joe about some business," he said. "I shan't be late." He added, "I'm meeting Harrison, you know, the City Councillor."

There was no response from the bedroom. Sarah wasn't there. She'd gone to the kitchen for Ronald's bottle. Jake experienced another wave of irritation. It was absurd, he thought angrily, that a man should be neglected within his own home. That child monopolised Sarah's attention.

He strode out of the room and went to the closet where he kept his heavy overcoat. It was a freezing night. He was about to put it on when he paused. He looked about him. Sarah was not in sight. With a brisk movement he ripped off one of the buttons. Then he went into the lounge.

He heard Sarah back in the bedroom, singing to herself as she tended the child.

"Sarah!" he called.

"Yes, dear."

"Please come here, I need you."

"In a minute . . ."

Jake sat in his favourite chair, the coat on his lap, a slight smile on his lips. He admired his inventiveness. No situation was too much for him, he thought with self-satisfaction.

Sarah came to him. "What is it, darling?" She raised her arms to adjust her hair, looking at him with enquiry.

Jake watched her as she made the simple, feminine gesture. She was a beauty. Even now, he could hardly believe his good fortune in having such an exceptional wife.

"It's this coat," he said, holding it out. "I'm going out and there's a button off. Would you fix it for me please?"

"Of course," she said.

She fetched the darning box, sat on the arm of his chair and sewed the button on. Jake watched her in silence. He felt consummately happy. His wife was by his side, working to please him.

This was how it had always been, before the baby came and diverted his wife's attention. But perhaps the kid wouldn't be such a darn nuisance once it became older.

"There you are," said Sarah, handing him the coat. She gazed at him, smiling. "Who was it you said you were going to see? I couldn't hear you properly."

"The City Councillor, Harrison," he said self-importantly.

Sarah frowned. "Oh, I didn't know you knew him."

"Oh yes," said Jake. "Met him last week at the lodge. We're good pals."

"Yes, of course," said Sarah. Her manner cooled. She went back to the baby. "Don't be too late."

Jake went to the *Record* office and left an envelope with

a fifty pence piece in it for the commissionaire to pass on to Thompson.

When Jake drove home, at ten thirty, he thought: I must find some way to meet Councillor Harrison. He ran through his list of useful contacts. Lurie might know him, in fact he was bound to, they were in the same business. Lurie could introduce him and it would be reasonably easy to bring him home to dinner. Harrison was sure to be the next Mayor. Sarah would like playing hostess to the First Citizen.

He felt warmth and affection for Sarah. At home, he joined his wife in bed and was about to kiss her when the baby started to cry. Sarah leaped from the bed to attend to it. Jake turned and lay silently, fuming. Eventually he fell into a restless sleep.

Ronald took the penny his father had given him and rushed outside. He could hear the tune of the ice-cream van as it approached. Ronald, with the enthusiasm of any four-year-old, shouted and waved his arms in case the ice-cream man didn't see him. Tommy, from up the street, walked over to him.

"Look," said Ronald, and waved the penny. Tommy watched him enviously.

When the ice-cream seller came along, Ronald gave him the penny. "A water ice," he said. The vendor passed him the triangular block. Ronald looked at it, then at his friend, Tommy, standing woebegone. "Cut it in half," he said impulsively.

Ronald took the two half ices and licked one. He gave the other to Tommy whose eyes lit up at the unexpected gift. The two boys ran down the pavement, laughing together.

From the window, Jake observed the scene. His eyes narrowed. He made his way downstairs and out of the front door.

"Ronald!" he called. His son turned and waved. "Come here at once!" he commanded. The boy ran to him, licking the remains of his ice from the stick.

"Yes, Daddy."

His father took him by the elbow and frog-marched him into the house. He closed the front door.

"I gave you money to buy yourself an ice-cream. To spend on yourself. What did you do? You wasted half of it on a complete stranger. Have you no sense of value?"

Ronald looked at his father in confusion. "But ..." He had nothing to say.

"Go to your room," said his father, his voice stern and unforgiving. "Stay there until I say you can come out."

Ronald walked slowly up the stairs to his room, went inside and closed the door. He sat disconsolately on the edge of his bed, the ice stick still in his hand. He couldn't understand what was so wrong with sharing his ice with Tommy. Daddy hadn't told him not to. But his father said it was wrong, so it must be. He felt very alone.

One year later, Uncle Leon came for Sunday lunch. Ronald liked his uncle and rushed outside to greet him. There was a buzz of conversation. Leon and his wife and their two children all came into the house.

When Leon left, later that day, he thrust a shilling into Ronald's hand. "Buy yourself some sweets," he said.

"Thanks, Uncle Leon," cried Ronald, excited at having so much for himself. He'd never had so much money before.

He bought sweets, lucky packets and bubble gum and in three days the money was gone. Exactly a week after Leon's visit, Jake called his son to him. Jake was seated in the old, sturdy armchair he favoured. He liked its heavy dependability. It made him feel magisterial. Ronald stood before his father, apprehensive but not knowing why.

"Your Uncle Leon gave you a shilling last week," said Jake. "It will be a good start to your savings. Bring it down to me, and I'll give you a two shilling piece for it."

"Yes, Daddy," said Ronald, fear fluttering.

"Where is it?" said Jake. "Don't you want me to double it for you, Ronald?"

Jake thought, as he watched the child cringe: That'll

give him something to think about. He's splurged it all on sweets. Ronald felt his guilt rise. He'd done wrong again. He hadn't realised the shilling couldn't be spent. Now, he dare not say that it was gone. What would his father do if he admitted it?

"It's in my room, Daddy," said Ronald, lying in desperation.

"Oh, really," said Jake, "Where in your room?"

"In the big cupboard," said Ronald, unable to bring himself to look into his father's eyes. "It's locked."

"Oh, it's locked. Good boy," said Jake, a smile in his voice. "You can go and play now, Ronald."

Relief leaping through him, the child ran outside. He felt he had just had a narrow escape.

Four days later, Ronald was playing cowboys with Tommy when he ran around a corner and collided with his father. Jake picked his son up. The boy was breathless from his exertions.

"Ronald," he said firmly. "That shilling in your cupboard. Why don't you bring it down. Don't you want two shillings for it?"

He put the child down. The boy looked at him, eyes wide and afraid.

"Don't just stand there. Go to your room, open the cupboard where you have the shilling locked away, and bring it to me. Hurry up!"

The authority in his voice sent the child scampering. As he ran to his bedroom Ronald thought: What can I do? I haven't got a shilling. His father had never struck him, yet he was petrified with fear. If I tell him I've spent the shilling he'll know I was lying last time.

In his room he leaned against the door, shaking with terror. I'll tell another lie, he thought, desperately. It worked last time. He waited a suitable time then walked downstairs. He approached his father who sat silently in the great chair.

"Well?" said Jake.

"I can't open the cupboard, Daddy," said Ronald in a small voice. "I've lost the key."

Jake's eyes bored into the child's face until Ronald stared down at the floor and shifted his feet.

Eventually, Jake spoke. "If you've lost the key, then we'll have to double the shilling some other time. You can go and play."

Ronald walked away. This time he felt no relief, only fear and guilt.

As the days went by, the small boy's mind was obsessed with thoughts of the shilling. Ronald began to allow himself the hope that his father had forgotten about it. Not a word was said for day after day, even though Ronald watched his father with apprehensive eyes whenever he saw him. But his father would greet him in his normal distant fashion, merely nodding his head.

On the seventh day Ronald was playing in the garden when he heard his father's voice: "Ronald! Come here!"

It seemed as though his heart stopped. He walked slowly toward the house, his feet scuffing the ground. He had no excuse left to make. To Ronald's amazement his father was smiling cheerfully.

"I've a nice surprise for you, Ronald."

The child thought: Perhaps it isn't about the shilling. He ventured a shaky smile in response to his father's cheerful attitude.

"Now," said his father, and put his hand in his side pocket.

"Look ... I've had another key made. It fits the cupboard in your room. Now we can go up together and take out the shilling."

Ronald went pale. His father took him by the shoulder and together they walked upstairs.

"I'm glad you were thoughtful enough to keep the cupboard locked," said his father. "Money should be looked after properly."

With great ceremony he brandished the key and slowly

fitted it into the lock. Ronald prayed silently: Please God, let it be the wrong key. The key turned. The child watched as though his life depended on it. It completed the circle and the cupboard door began to open, slowly.

"Now, where did you put it?" asked his father.

Ronald stood, dumb, terrified, his mind blank. He watched his father peering with elaborate pretence into every corner of the cupboard, feeling with his hands. Finally his father turned to him.

"You were lying, Ronald. All this time, nothing but lies."

Ronald felt his father's hand descend on his shoulder and propel him down the stairs, through the kitchen and out into the back garden where his mother sat reading.

"Sarah," he heard his father say. "Ronald has something to say."

Ronald looked up in fresh anguish. What was he supposed to say?

"Tell your mother," and his father paused: "I am a terrible liar. Come on!"

"I am a terrible liar," said Ronald. "I told my father I had a shilling. I told my father I had a shilling. But I spent it all on sweets. I spent it all on sweets." Ronald began to cry.

"He didn't even have the courage to admit it," said his father. "He told me lie after lie about locking it in a cupboard and then losing the key. That boy will never be any good."

Ronald saw his mother's expression become stern. "You should never tell lies, Ronald. There's no need to ever lie to your own father and mother. Go to your room, and stay there."

The boy walked away. His father shouted after him: "Tomorrow I'll show you what happens to liars and cheats!"

The next morning Ronald was awake at first light. His father had said he was going to show him what happened to liars and cheats. Slowly, time passed. Finally, his father came for him.

They drove to a part of the city Ronald had never seen before. His father maintained a forbidding silence, looking straight ahead as he drove. Eventually he parked the car outside an old building. A sign said: Netherton Hall. The walls were dark brown, stained and discoloured by the weather. His father led the way and walked without hesitation through the front door. He spoke to a man on duty in the hall.

Ronald looked about him in fear and mistrust. What sort of place was this? It smelled old and damp. The small lights high in the ceiling created weird shadows. There were stains on the floorboards. Everything seemed dismal.

Ronald's father's hand descended on his shoulder and they began to explore the building. His father opened doors and let him inside. There were boys, some his own age, others older, in clothes the colour of sacking. All were dressed identically and all wore huge boots with studs. None of the boys smiled. Their eyes were all dull.

"You see those children?" said Jake.

"Yes, Daddy," said Ronald tremulously.

"They're all cheats and liars like you."

Ronald said nothing. He felt dizzy, but his father's firm grip kept him upright.

They continued their tour through the rambling old building. They went everywhere, into the stinking lavatories, through the dormitories, sourly smelling of old bedding and dirty feet, and finally back into the dim hallway where the old man sat in a cubicle. Ronald wanted to run out to escape from this awful place. But his father was talking to him.

"Remember this place, Ronald. It's a reformatory. Boys like you are sent here to be punished."

Ronald looked at his father. He hung on his every word.

"If you ever misbehave again, Ronald," said his father, making each word count, "I will send you here until you grow up."

Ronald looked wildly about him, at the dank corridors leading to all kinds of unimaginable horrors. He was terrified. He closed his eyes to shut out the fear.

When they were back home Ronald walked slowly to his room and lay face down on the bed. He had lived a nightmare. Every day, for weeks to come, he thought of the reformatory.

Tommy went in search of Ronald. He found him at the old canal. Tommy sat on the edge of the canal, watching Ronald without announcing himself. He was puzzled by Ronald's behaviour. He was walking in a strange way, moving forward, then dodging to one side, taking long, awkward strides and then short quick ones.

Tommy shouted: "Ron! What are you doing!"

Ronald stopped and looked at him guiltily.

"I'm just walking," he said.

"You're walking funny," said Tommy and laughed. He joined Ronald on the expanse of cement. It was veined with multitudes of tiny cracks where the cement had split.

Ronald continued with his peculiar walk. He was avoiding the cracks. He couldn't explain it to Tommy, and in any case he didn't want to. It was just that he knew that something disastrous would happen if he stepped in the cracks and something good if he avoided them. But there were so many cracks they were not easy to avoid. He walked carefully between them, lost in concentration.

"Come on, Ron," shouted Tommy. "That's a stupid game. Let's find the ball."

Ronald followed his friend and they ran off together.

It was Christmas Eve, a time for giving and receiving of presents. Ronald was so excited at the prospect of waking up on Christmas morning to open his Christmas stocking, he went to bed especially early. His parents were expecting friends, and later in the evening would move on to other people's homes. Ronald lay in bed, wide awake, but determined not to be. He knew that the sooner he fell asleep, the sooner the next morning would arrive. Finally, sleep came.

The first dim rays of dawn fell into Ronald's room.

He woke up, stretching and yawning. Then, with a

young child's alertness, he was wide awake. Full of eagerness and anticipation he jumped out of bed.

There, hanging on his dressing-table, was a large red
Christmas stocking.

Heart pounding, eyes shining, Ronald reached up and
detached the heavy stocking. He carried it with the
intention of emptying the presents on the floor. As he was
about to do so, he was surprised to see a trickle of fine
black powder. Ronald put the stocking down and touched
the small black mound which had fallen on the carpet.

It was coal dust.

Coal dust? He was totally bewildered. He picked up the
stocking and upended it. Out fell pieces of coal, onions,
leeks, carrots, potato peelings, and other assorted detritus
of the kitchen. The stocking fell to the ground. Ronald
knelt, staring at the rubbish. He felt a turning and twisting
in his stomach. Tears came to his eyes. Why had he been
given rubbish for Christmas?

He carefully scooped up the debris and carried it
through the early-morning silence of the house into the
kitchen. He opened the grate of the big stove and threw
everything into the flames. Ronald washed his hands in
the kitchen sink and dried them carefully. He went to his
room and sat silently looking through the window at the
softly falling snow. The neighbourhood became alive as
the morning grew older. He stayed in the chair, un-
moving. Christmas was no longer a magical time.

Ronald heard his mother calling him for breakfast. His
mother and father were already seated at the table.

He took his place.

"Good morning, Ronald," said his father cheerfully.

"Good morning, Dad," he said softly.

"Merry Christmas, my boy!"

His mother approached the table from the kitchen and
put his plate in front of him.

"Well, cheer up," said his father, regarding him with
amusement. He put down his knife and fork and leaned
across the table. "How did you like your Christmas
stocking?"

"I burned it," said Ronald, with so much emotion that the words came out muffled.

"What did you say?" demanded his father.

"It was rubbish so I burned it," said Ronald, audibly this time.

Ronald's father stood up so suddenly that his knife clattered to the floor.

"You burned it? You say you burned it!"

"Yes, Dad," said Ronald, thrown off balance by his father's violent reaction.

Ronald saw his mother standing next to the table, watching the tableau between father and son.

"My God!" cried his father, picking up his napkin and throwing it onto the table. "That's five pounds up in smoke!"

"I ... I don't understand," said Ronald, shakily. "It was only rubbish."

"If you'd taken the trouble to look instead of being spiteful, you would have found a five-pound note inside that stocking," said his father leaning toward him in the intensity of his anger. "Five pounds!" He shouted the words.

Ronald was plunged into a maelstrom of bewilderment and confusion. He had thought that a horrible trick had been played on him, and now it appeared that *he* was the guilty one! He had done wrong by burning the stocking. Five pounds! He thought carefully but could remember no sign of a five-pound note. Perhaps it was hidden in the coal ... He looked at his father. He was numb with helplessness.

His father stalked out of the room. Ronald glanced appealingly at his mother. She stood, silent, watching him with troubled eyes.

When Ronald was thirteen, he received a gift of a five-pound deposit in a post office savings bank. He liked the official look of the bank book, the post office crest and the neat writing stating that five pounds stood to his credit. He used to carry it about with him.

A few days after his birthday it was announced that all schoolchildren were to be evacuated to a place in the country to protect them from Nazi bombing raids, which were considered likely in the near future. The boys from the Royal Grammar School were to go to Penrith, in the Lake District, and the girls from the Central High School to Keswick, fifteen miles from Penrith.

Jake and Sarah debated whether it would be wise to bring Ronald back for the Christmas holidays.

"I think it would be quite safe," said Sarah. "The Germans haven't dropped any bombs yet. It seems hysterical, sending the children into the country."

"You can never be too careful, Sarah," said Jake. "We might bring Ronald home and out of the blue there could be an air raid. Leave him where he is. I'm sure he'll amuse himself."

"All the other children are coming back, I hear," said Sarah.

"Safety first," said Jake. "Let's keep him out of the line of fire."

"All right," said Sarah.

For three weeks Ronald was the only boy at the Penrith hostel. He walked around kicking stones and watching cows. He was glad when the other boys returned from their Christmas holidays. Those parents who could afford to move from the city followed their children into the country. But instead of going to Penrith, where the boys were housed, Jake and Sarah decided to settle in Keswick, where the girls were accommodated.

"After all," said Jake, when they discussed it. "Harry and his wife, and the Harrises and the Luries are all there. It's a coincidence that all their children are girls. If we stayed at Penrith we'd be travelling to Keswick every night to be with our friends."

So Jake and Sarah went to Keswick while Ronald attended school in Penrith.

The next school holidays, Jake and Sarah were staying with friends in Keswick and it was arranged that Ronald's grandmother should take him to the seaside. Jake had

179

given Ronald an allowance of sixpence a day while he was at the resort.

On the first day, Ronald set out to explore. He found the amusement park on the beach. It was noisy and cheerful and exciting. People were playing pin-ball machines and various games of skill. Bells were clanging, people were talking loudly and noisy music was being played. With his six pennies he tried various machines. The first was a fruit machine. You put in a penny, pulled the handle and hoped that three similar fruits would appear in a row. That didn't appeal to him very much. On the next machine you had to try and catch a penny in a clown's mouth.

Next to Ronald another boy was playing a game in which you rolled a penny down a chute on to a board consisting of a number of squares. If the penny landed in the middle of a square, you won two pennies. If it touched or covered any of the lines which marked the sides of the square, you lost.

This game had a curious appeal for Ronald. As soon as the boy finished his game, and lost, Ronald took his place. He watched his penny roll down the chute and spin dizzily on the board. It lurched drunkenly as gravity gradually pulled it down. Ronald felt an anxious exhilaration as the coin hesitated on a line and then twisted unexpectedly toward the middle of the square—but 'all' would be lost if the coin fell on the line.

The coin stayed in the centre. Ronald had won.

Eagerly he played again, and lost. He lost twice more, then his sixpence was gone. Ronald felt frustration. He wanted to experience again the anxious exhilaration of waiting to see whether the coin would fall in the right or the wrong place. As he stood in the amusement arcade he remembered his bank book which he had been carrying with him for several months. He felt in the pocket of his blazer. There it was. He opened it and looked at the annotation. Five pounds. He took the book to the post office, presented it and withdrew some money. An entry was made in the book.

Ronald frittered away the five pounds, most of it on the gambling machines, but he had an enjoyable holiday.

Back at Penrith, Ronald needed his bicycle and his typewriter. His bicycle he could fetch next time he went on holiday, but in the meantime he wanted his typewriter as he enjoyed writing plays. The previous year he had used the typewriter to write a play which the school principal liked. It was performed at the school's annual festival. Ronald wrote to his father asking him if he would please send the typewriter. He received no reply, so after a few weeks he wrote again. Still no reply.

Then came the half-term holidays and Ronald was allowed to visit his parents. As soon as he had greeted his mother, Ronald ran to his room to look at his typewriter. All the way home he'd been bubbling with ideas for a play. He wanted to write them before they faded away.

There was no sign of the typewriter. He looked everywhere. It was gone. Ronald went to his father.

"Dad," he said, with trepidation. Every conversation with his father was fraught with tension, and Ronald was never sure what course a talk with him would take.

"What is it?" said his father, looking up from his newspaper.

"I can't find my typewriter. I want to use it."

"Oh," his father put down the paper. "I've sold it."

Ronald was flabbergasted. "Why did you do that, Dad?"

"It's wartime, Ronald. Nobody can get typewriters any more. They're worth a lot of money. I did the sensible thing and sold it at a very good price."

His father resumed his reading. It seemed that the conversation was closed. Ronald could not make sense out of his father's explanation. After all, his father had not bought the typewriter. It was a present to Ronald from someone else. Now his father had sold it, apparently for a lot of money. Why didn't his father give him the money? It was baffling, but obviously his father knew what he was doing.

Towards the end of the holidays, Ronald approached his father again and asked if he could take his bicycle back to

181

school with him. He explained that all the boys had bikes so that they could ride around the countryside at the weekends. His father told him that would be impossible.

"I'm using the bicycle to go fishing," he said. "It saves my petrol ration."

"All right," said Ronald. He was disconsolate. No type-writer and no bicycle.

One night, Sarah asked Ronald: "Is everything all right in Penrith? Are they looking after you?"

"Yes, Mum," he said. "It's fine in the country. We all share a huge dormitory."

"Do you have everything you need?"

"Yes," he said. Ronald looked around the table. There seemed to be no shortage of food, not like the hostel, where the rations were small and the food boring. But, like most children, Ronald accepted whatever life offered at the time.

"As long as you're not going short," said his mother.

Ronald was watching his father, who had been grimly silent for quite a while.

"On your birthday," his father said, "Uncle Ernie gave you a Post Office savings book."

"Yes, father," said Ronald. He felt the now familiar sense of anxiety. What had he done wrong? He glanced desperately at his mother. She was looking at his father.

Frank produced a brand new £5 note. "I want to double Uncle Ernie's money, so I'll put this five pounds into your bank book for you."

He looked at Ronald with a broad smile. "Bring me the book down," he said.

Ronald panicked. He looked his father in the eye. "I don't have it. It's at the hostel."

"Oh," said his father. "Don't forget to post it to me as soon as you get back, then I'll double your money and return the book to you."

"Yes, Father," said Ronald, thinking: I can't send it. I've spent the money. He'll hate me again. Despair welled within him. Why could he do nothing right? Why couldn't

182

he ever please his father? The next day he returned to the hostel.

He sat on his bunk and looked at the post office book. Every withdrawal he had made in the holiday resort was neatly entered with the stamp of the resort office branch. How could he send this incriminating document to his father. Yet he knew his father would pursue the subject until the missing five pounds was accounted for. Ronald had been back at school only a few days when a letter arrived. It said: I need your savings book because I have to complete my income tax return. Please send it immediately.

Three days later a post card arrived. It contained one message, printed on every available inch of space on the card: Send post office book, send post office book, send post office book, send post office book, send post office book ... As he turned the card in his hands, the slogan leaped at him from every angle. Ronald felt a sickness, a feeling of being hunted and cornered without any hope of escape. He flung the card on his bed. There had to be something he could do. Where could a schoolboy obtain five pounds ... a fortune?

He'd go to work. That was it! He remembered a teacher announcing that to help the war effort, schoolboy volunteers were needed for farm work. The pay was fivepence an hour. Hope sprang. Perhaps he could make five pounds after all, and put it back in his post office savings account. His father need never know about his criminal action in spending it.

He worked out the arithmetic. At fivepence an hour, it would take him more than two hundred hours to earn five pounds. He might be able to obtain three or four hours' work a day, because it was summer and the days were long. He wrote a letter to his father in a bid to gain time. He said he had mislaid the savings book but would search for its among his things and send it soon.

Ronald worked in the fields every day after school picking potatoes. The letters from his father arrived regularly, every few days, repeating the demand for the post office book like a litany. Send the book! Where is the book! I must have the book!

Spurred by this postal bombardment, Ronald deposited every penny he earned in his savings account. Eventually, he had five pounds. In his moment of triumph, Ronald, with the bank book in his hands, realised the flaw in his plan. The book gave a detailed record of his withdrawals. Even with the five pounds, his father would know what he had done. He would have to acquire another savings book. The instructions said that in case of loss or theft, the holder of the book should write, giving details and obtain a replacement.

Ronald tore up the savings book and flushed every scrap down the toilet. He wrote to the post office authorities, saying he had lost his book and asked for a replacement. In a few days the new book arrived. Ronald opened it. It contained one notation only, in copper-plate handwriting— Credit: Five Pounds.

He jumped into the air with relief. He'd done it! Five pounds and a clean book! It felt as though a huge weight had been lifted from his shoulders. He posted the savings book with a simple covering note: "Dear Dad, I found the book, Love Ronald."

For the first time in weeks, Ronald took part in horse-play with the other children and slept without disturbing dreams. Four days later, Ronald received a letter from his mother, saying, among other things, how pleased his father was to have finally received the savings book.

Two weeks after that, Ronald received another letter. This time from his father.

It said: "Looking at your savings book, I saw that the five pounds was deposited at Penrith post office, not in Ashby where your Uncle Ernie lives. I wrote to the post office and they have provided me with the full details of your transactions."

The general tenor of the letter was that the episode proved Ronald was not to be trusted. No mention was made of his earning and replacing the money.

Because he now had no typewriter, Ronald's artistic

interests became diverted in directions other than writing. He began to make rugs, and to work hard at his art classes.

Soon after his fourteenth birthday, the British Ministry of Information announced a nationwide poster contest for 'Warships Week'. Ronald entered.

During the holidays he took his paints home with him. On his first evening he was busily drawing and colouring when he heard his father enter the room.

"What are you up to?" his father asked.

Ronald explained that he was trying out designs for a poster.

Looking at his son's drawings, Jake was strangely impressed. Perhaps Ronald had the makings of an artist. It was an outside chance, but perhaps his son would finally do something he could be proud of.

He thought for a moment, examining the tentative drawings Ronald had made.

"I'll tell you what," said Jake, "I'll make a bargain with you."

"What's that, Dad?" asked Ronald, watching his father with anxiety. What was his father up to now?

"If you win this contest—not that I think you have a chance—but if you do actually win it, I'll buy you the biggest artist's set that money can buy."

"Thanks, Dad," said Ronald. "I don't know if I can, but I'll certainly try." He felt pleased by his father's approval. By offering to reward him if he won, his father was admitting the possibility that he *could* win.

He drew poster after poster, rejecting those that weren't his very best. Eventually he decided and posted one off to the contest.

"You don't really think you're going to win, do you?" asked his father.

"Don't dash his hopes, Jake," said Sarah. "I thought it was very good.

Ronald sat silently. He was proud of what he'd drawn.

Some weeks later Ronald won the competition. His poster had been judged the best and it was published in the newspapers.

Ronald was back at school at the time. When he found out the result, he immediately wrote to his father telling him the particular artist's set he wanted as his reward. At home, Jake showed the newspaper announcing the award to his friends and business acquaintances. At the next Lodge meeting he produced it.

"First in the country," said Jake. (Actually it was first in the county.) "That's not a small achievement you know. There was tens of thousands of entries."

Lurie patted him on the back in jocular fashion. "Well done, Jake, we all knew you had it in you."

"Thank you," said Jake, and Lurie was taken aback. His oblique joke had been taken literally. Jake regarded Ronald's accomplishment as his own.

Jake never did buy Ronald the artist's set he'd promised.

At school, Ronald and the other boys of his age were beginning to notice the opposite sex. Everyone's favourite was the house mistress, the quality of whose feminine appeal was somewhat exaggerated by her being the only woman there. Gladys Brown was a friendly woman who was fond of the dozens of gawky adolescent boys. She often caught them staring at her, blushing and averting their eyes when she noticed. She liked to make them feel at ease.

Ronald was one of her favourites. She made him feel important by sending him on errands. One day she asked him to buy some soap powder for her. "All right, Mrs Brown," he said. "I won't forget."

Gladys had made her request to Ronald during the dinner break. There was one more class before he would be able to go out and buy the powder. Sitting at his desk, Ronald realised that the house mistress had forgotten to give him any money. He had already spent his week's allowance. Anxious guilt descended like a familiar mantle.

He sat, oblivious to the teacher's words, thinking of his dilemma. He couldn't let Gladys down. He *had* to buy the soap powder for her. He knew that he could not possibly go back and ask her for the money. There was not time. Not having money of his own was a state of guilt. He could not worsen it by admitting that he had already spent his week's pocket money, instead of making it last.

He sat, pondering, driven by a desperate need not to lose Gladys's approval, which he would surely forfeit if he returned without the soap powder. Ronald put up his hand.

"May I be excused, sir? I want to leave the room."

The teacher nodded permission. Ronald got up, walked toward the toilet and entered the hallway, where the boys' coats were hung. Methodically, he began to rifle the pockets. Most of them were empty but Ronald collected a penny here, two pennies there. Slowly the total built up. He needed ninepence for the soap powder.

He had eightpence. One penny to go. He approached the last coat in the row. If this coat contained no money he was done for. He put his hand into the deep pocket and felt a coin. Triumphantly he pulled it out. A hand seized his wrist.

"So that's what you've been up to, Marcus. Pinching, eh!"

It was a prefect. He'd been caught red-handed. Ronald was called before the headmaster.

"Stealing is a serious offence, Marcus," said the master, his expression grave. "But I have decided, in this case, that expulsion would be too extreme a punishment. You are suspended for a period of a fortnight."

The headmaster shuffled the papers on the desk.

"Your explanation of why you stole the other boys' money is odd, but it does appear that you were motivated by a misguided desire to please. I must warn you however that any repetition will result in your instant expulsion." He paused, solemnly.

"Your parents shall be informed, by letter."

For several weeks prior to this disaster, Ronald had been working on a rug for his mother. Now, on his last day at school, he worked with feverish speed to complete the gift. On the train journey home he clutched the rug in

187

both hands, as if it might shield him from his father's wrath. As he approached his parents' house, his suitcase in one hand, the rug in the other, he was terribly afraid. The compulsion was to flee, to turn and run. He stood, hesitating, outside the door. Then he opened it and went inside.

Ronald put down his suitcase and carefully hid the rug out of sight in the hallway. His parents were in the lounge. Nervously he walked forward. His father looked up, smiling. "Hello Ronald! Don't stand there, come on in!"

His mother stood and walked toward him.

"Are you hungry, dear?" she asked.

He nodded.

"I'll fix you a snack," she said. "Just to see you through to dinner time."

"Thank you, Mum," he said. Ronald had expected the worst. Criticism, ostracism, angry words. But his mother was exactly as she always was, and his father was, incredibly, friendlier than he had ever been. Ronald had tea and buns and listened to his parents' casual conversation about the events of home and business. Later, they had dinner and he ate hungrily after the spare rations at the school.

Midway through the evening, as his mother sat and read and his father studied figures in one of his innumerable black books, Ronald remembered the rug. He felt pleasant anticipation. Quietly he went to the hall. He picked up the rug, unrolled it and looked at it once again. It was a fine rug, he thought with the pride of a craftsman. Holding it out between his arms he walked smilingly into the lounge.

"I have a present for you, Mum," he said cheerily. "It's a rug. I've worked on it all term."

His mother looked up from her book. His father stood up swiftly. "Stole it, more likely!" he cried, and wrenching the rug from Ronald, threw it in the coal bin. In the strained silence of the room he looked at Ronald grimly. There was no trace of his earlier goodwill. Sarah was looking from father to son with an expression of astonishment.

188

"What is it, Jake?" she asked. "I don't understand . . ."

Jake produced a letter from his inside pocket.

"This explains it," he said. "It's a letter from the school. In black and white. Your son is a thief. He was caught stealing money from other boys. Now he has the damned cheek to come home offering presents, when he knows he's been suspended from school." He gave the letter to his wife. She read it, her face white.

"It's a miracle he wasn't expelled." said Ronald's father, glaring at him.

Sarah finished the letter. Ronald looked at the white testimonial to his guilt, crumpled in her hand. He could imagine the words.

"Go to your room," said his mother, not looking at him.

He turned, and made his familiar way to isolation. Ronald spent most of the two weeks of his suspension gloomily in his room.

Back at school again, Ronald came up against a wall of hostility from the other boys. He was known, now, as 'the chap who pinched the pocket money'. Toward the end of term, Ronald came across a magazine called *Health and Efficiency*. It was a naturist publication and it contained photographs of nude men and women. The sight of naked female bodies aroused him sexually and he masturbated.

The housekeeper found the magazine in his drawer and reported Ronald to the headmaster. Masturbation was regarded as a heinous offence. After his previous misdemeanour, it was unpardonable. Ronald was expelled. The disaster confirmed Ronald's low opinion of himself. His father was right, as usual. Ronald was worthless, no good to anyone, least of all to himself.

Ronald's final disgrace at school exploded his father's wrath. Ronald stood hang-dog, staring hopelessly at the carpet as his fathered berated him. During his father's harangue, Ronald saw his mother shaking her head, in final disapproval of her son.

Jake announced that rather than have Ronald 'hanging

about the place', he had arranged for him to stay with relatives in Edinburgh for several weeks. In Edinburgh, Ronald found his cousins to be cheerful, friendly people. His Uncle, Robert, was particularly helpful and encouraging.

One evening Robert took him to 'the dogs'. Ronald was fascinated by the atmosphere at the greyhound racing track. He placed small bets and won every time. He excitedly collected his winnings and rushed to inspect the dogs competing in the next race. The occasion was a challenge and a thrill—an easy way to get rich quickly, or so it seemed to Ronald. He studied form, and went with Robert twice a week to the dog track. Ronald's luck held, and by the time he was to return home, he was well ahead. The visit to Edinburgh was one of the happiest times Ronald had ever had in his life.

He came home to discover that his father had arranged 'digs' for him in the city.

"Even though you have been expelled," his father said, "you can still sit your School Leaving Certificate examination. It's up to you to get your head down and study hard."

Ronald looked at his father. The blows of guilt and disgrace he had received in recent months had served to stiffen his spirit. By some strange alchemy he had become wary of his father, suspicious of his motives, alert for deviousness. Now, he waited for one of his father's familiar inducements. Jake never made a suggestion without an inducement.

"I'll tell you what I'm going to do," said his father.

Ronald thought: Here it comes.

"I'll give you twenty-five pounds if you pass your certificate," said his father grandly.

He held up a hand, as though to keep Ronald's thanks at bay. Ronald had no intention of speaking.

"I'll do even better than that!" said Jake. "If you get any distinctions, I'll double it. You'll get fifty pounds! Think of that," he said, his eyes glittering. "Fifty pounds! That's worth working for, isn't it?"

It would be, thought Ronald sourly, if I'd ever receive it. He became aware of a perverse spirit of independence. I'll show him, he thought. I'll study hard, I'll pass that exam, I'll get distinctions and when he doesn't produce the fifty pounds I won't even remind him about it. He thought triumphantly: I'll study for *myself* ... I'll do it for *me!* I don't need bribes.

"All right, father," he said. He saw his father's eyes shine with triumph. "I'll try."

His father nodded approvingly.

With diligence and perseverance which surprised even himself, Ronald set about his studies. He wrote the examinations confidently and gained a distinction in every subject.

The reward which his father had promised him, never materialised. Ronald never mentioned the subject. One day he noticed his father studying him speculatively. Ronald grinned inwardly. He felt he had turned the tables on his father.

One day Ronald had been visiting his parents and was about to go back to his digs when his mother called him.

"Ronald," she said. "Here's the ten pounds for your rent. Please pay it tomorrow."

"All right, Mum," he said.

The next night was dog racing night. Ronald went to the track and by the third race had lost all his betting money. He remembered the ten pounds for the rent, folded in his wallet. On impulse he put it on a 'certainty' for the fourth race which would return the ten pounds with a nice profit. The dog ran last. He left the meeting penniless.

Some time later Ronald was in his room when there was a knock on the door. He opened it and saw his parents. Sarah looked at him accusingly.

"Why didn't you pay the rent?" she asked.

Ronald didn't know how to tell her. His father began to shout. "What did you do with the money?"

"I lost it at the dogs," he said, ashamed, feeling the now familiar guilt and anxiety.

"At the *dogs?*" said Jake incredulously. "D'you mean to say you took the money for your rent and *gambled* it away?"

"Yes."

His father stepped back, in shock. "You must be out of your mind," he said, his voice hushed. "No normal being would gamble with his *rent* money!"

Sarah moved to her husband's side. They stood close together, regarding with awe the creature they had brought into the world.

"You'll have to come back home, Ronald," said his mother. "If we can't even trust you to pay the rent ..." Her voice trailed into uncertainty.

Installed once more in his old room at home, Ronald found the atmosphere of his parents' house stifling after the freedom he had enjoyed in digs. He managed to slip away and gamble whatever money he had on dog racing. His initial good luck had now vanished and everything he ventured he lost.

One holiday weekend Jake and Sarah decided to spend three days with friends in the country. Ronald was left behind, alone in the house. After his parents had gone, he sat in the lounge, not knowing what to do. There was a race meeting that day, but he didn't have any money.

"Why do you need cash?" asked his father when he had brought up the subject. "The kitchen's loaded with food. You won't want for anything."

Ronald stretched out on the sofa and put his feet up. He was bored and restless. His eyes fell on a cigarette box on the mantelpiece. It was one of his father's treasured possessions. Ronald looked closely at the box. It was solid silver, and heavy.

This must be worth a lot of money, he thought. The exciting idea of a day at the races clouded his thinking. If he could raise some money on the cigarette box he could go to the dogs and win enough to redeem the box, bring it home and he would have money to spare. He would make some money and his father would be none the wiser. Impetuously he took the cigarette box to a pawn-broker.

The pawnbroker inspected the box thoroughly. "I'll lend you five pounds on it," he said, disinterestedly.

"That's fine," said Ronald, thinking: It's worth a lot more than that, but it doesn't matter because I'll be back to collect it on Monday.

He took the crisp five-pound note and tucked it in his pocket. He went to the course and by the fifth race he was winning sixty pounds. He soared with confidence. He would make a real killing. He put fifty pounds on a twenty to one outsider. The dog ran second.

In the next race, Ronald picked another outsider which seemed to have a good chance—at twenty-five to one. He calculated: If he placed the remaining ten pounds winnings on it, he would win two hundred and fifty pounds. He thought deeply. No. That's wasn't enough. He'd find a dog with better odds. He settled for a thirty-three to one shot and placed his bet. "Fifteen pounds on the nose" he said. The bookie gave him his ticket.

The traps opened and the electric hare scooted in front of the greyhounds in their brightly coloured coats.

The race was over. His dog wasn't in the first four. Ronald stood among the milling crowd, his hands in his empty pockets. He'd lost the five pounds he came with, and the sixty pounds he'd won. Strangely, he didn't feel depressed. He felt all right. It was during the long walk home (he didn't even have bus fare) that he thought of the silver cigarette box and his father and what would happen when he came home and found it missing. Butterflies of fear fluttered in his stomach.

Ronald lay on his bed, his hands behind his neck. He waited for the inevitable. He'd heard his parents arrive half an hour earlier.

"Ronald! Are you there?" his mother had shouted, as she opened the door.

"Yes, Mum, I'm here!" he replied, from his room.

"We're back," she said, unnecessarily.

There were sounds of them moving around the house, carrying in suitcases. He heard his mother put on the kettle. Ronald heard muted words between his parents.

"Sarah!" It was his father's voice. Ronald cringed as though struck.

"What is it?" he heard his mother say.

"The cigarette box. It's not here. What did you do with it?"

"I haven't touched it, Jake. It must be somewhere."

Ronald listened to his parents walking about and moving things in their search. He rolled on his stomach and pulled the pillow over his head. He couldn't block the sounds from below. He heard his mother's and father's voices rising in volume, his father's predominating.

"I tell you, Sarah, it's him. You know what he's like. Who else would take it?"

His father's voice roared through the house: "Ronald! Come here at once!"

Ashen-faced, hands shaking, Ronald got off the bed, opened his door and walked downstairs. His facial expression was his confession.

There was a silence as he stood in front of his parents. His father was flushed with rage. His mother looked about to faint.

"He stole it, Sarah!" said Jake. "Your son stole from us. What did you do with it, eh?" His voice rose to a scream. "You've squandered it at the dogs haven't you? You're demented, that's what you are."

Jake's rage moved from heat to ice.

"I've told you all along Sarah, Ronald is no good. He's worthless. He's not a man. And you always speak up for him."

Ronald tried to remember his mother standing up for him. He couldn't think. In the midst of the turbulence swirling around him, Ronald was paradoxically calm. He had done what he had done. Now he was a spectator.

"This time he has gone too far." There was a strange note

in Jake's voice. Exultation. Triumph. Victory over the enemy.

"What are you going to do, Jake?" His mother's voice was anxious.

"I'm going to put Ronald in a sanatorium where he can receive expert care and have discipline forced into him."

"Is there such a place?" she asked.

"Yes. Creighton Royal, in Dumfries."

"Oh Jake, you can't be serious!" said Sarah. She looked at him for a long moment. Then she said, softly, "Not that place."

"I don't care," said Jake. "Dr Robinson recommends it and he's an expert. He says that Ronald is a compulsive gambler and that the psychiatrists at Dumfries are excellent. They might be able to untangle whatever mess he calls his brain."

Jake was silent under his wife's accusing stare. He waved his arms in aggravation. "Even you, Sarah, have to admit that his behaviour isn't normal! Stealing from his own parents to go and gamble!" He shook his head, still appalled by the thought of Ronald's crime.

They discussed the plan and eventually Sarah agreed that if Dr Robinson recommended it, it must be right. Ronald knew that his parents didn't know what to do with him. His attitude was a numb acceptance. He had just turned sixteen, yet already his world was upside down. It was agreed. Ronald would leave at the weekend for Creighton Royal in Dumfries, the rest home for people with bad nerves.

There was a long curving driveway leading to Creighton Royal. People were strolling on the green lawns, some in dressing-gowns, others more formally dressed. Ronald saw a little man in shorts and vest jogging down the driveway. The man turned the corner and was lost to view. A nurse at the reception desk asked him to be seated. After a few minutes, a tall, shambling figure smoking a pipe and sloppily dressed in a sports coat and corduroys introduced himself: Dr Palfrey.

"So you're young Marcus, eh?" He clapped Ronald on the shoulder. "You'll like it here. Bit crowded, though, with all the chaps from the war."

He was friendly, if vague. Ronald took to him at once. After chatting to Ronald for a while, Dr Palfrey introduced him to another doctor, Dr Collingworth, who was short, clean-shaven and wore rimless spectacles. He had a sad face, with a mouth which drooped at the corners. He spoke quickly and intensely.

"Right, Ronald," he said, "first things first. I'll show you where you'll be sleeping." He took him to a small, tidy room with only basic furniture.

"We'll probably leave you very much to yourself young fellow," he said, taking off his glasses and polishing them. Ronald was soon to discover that this was a ritual with Dr Collingworth. He polished his glasses during every conversation.

Ronald looked around him, as he stood outside the great mansion with its colonnaded entrance. A pretty nurse in a starched uniform came past. She smiled at him cheerily. "Hello," she said. Ronald smiled back. She has nice legs, he thought.

He began to think he might enjoy himself at Creighton Royal. Ronald walked along the corridor which led to his room. It was a long, rambling wing of the building. As he turned a corner he almost bumped into a florid old gentleman with wispy white hair. The man peered at him.

"I don't seem to recognise the face," he said in pontifical tones. "Have we met before?"

"No, sir, we haven't," said Ronald. "I'm new here."

"Oh! Good show, young fellow," he said, beaming, to reveal a shiny set of false teeth. "You'll be happy here, I'm sure. We're a big jolly family." He paused, glanced about him, and leaned forward confidentially. "What's your problem, my boy?"

"Nerves," said Ronald. He didn't want to say: "Gambling."

"Nerves, eh?" He stroked a palm across the pink skin

of his balding head. "Lot of bad nerves about these days. Must be the war, y'know."

He glanced around him, with a furtive air. Then straightened himself and announced: "Let me introduce myself. Admiral Henderson. Pleased to meet you." He stuck out a hand and Ronald grasped it.

A real admiral. He felt thrilled to be in the presence of such a distinguished man.

"It's a great honour to meet you, sir," he said, and they shook hands gravely.

"Well," said the admiral, "I don't suffer from nerves, I'm glad to say. But I do have a most upsetting ailment."

The dignified figure fell into step beside Ronald and they paced down the long corridor.

"You won't be seeing much of me," the admiral said portentously, shaking his head.

"I'm receiving treatment for a terrible hernia."

"Quite often my guts come bulging out through a hole in my stomach and fall over the floor."

Admiral Henderson gestured eloquently with his hands, miming the emergence of yards of intestines.

"The trouble is," he said seriously, "it takes so long to pack them in again. It often takes all day."

Ronald looked at the old gentleman with amazement. What an astonishing illness! He'd never heard of such a complaint.

"So if you don't see me about," said Admiral Henderson, "don't worry about me. I'll be busy pushing my insides back. Deuced difficult job, y'know. Have to be careful to put everything in the right place."

Admiral Henderson turned smartly. "Oh well, I must be off. Nice meeting you! A pleasure to see a new face." He made off briskly down the corridor.

What an interesting place this is, thought Ronald. The admiral was lucky that a hospital existed, where he could be treated. He went to his room and unpacked. Having done everything, he sat aimlessly on the bed. No one appeared to tell him what to do, so he wandered outside again.

Among the people at the entrance to the building he saw Dr Collingworth, chatting to various groups. Ronald assumed this was visitors' day, it being Sunday.

Eventually, Collingworth headed in his direction. "Settled in all right?"

"Yes, sir," he said.

"There's no particular routine, here, Ronald, so don't stand on ceremony. Meal times are fixed, there are special therapy classes, but everything else is unconventional. I'm sure you'll soon find your own niche." With that, he gave a wave and walked off.

As Ronald turned a corner, he saw the little man he had seen when he arrived. He was still clad in shorts and vest and was doing continuous press-ups on the lawn. His body was knotted with muscles. As he watched, the lithe figure sprang to his feet and headed down the path at a jog-trot. That man must be really fit, thought Ronald. He went back to his room and waited for dinner. The fresh air was making him hungry.

During dinner that evening Ronald was seated at a table with three other people, all considerably older than he. Two were quiet, sombre gentlemen who looked at him listlessly when he introduced himself and mumbled their names in acknowledgment. When they had finished eating they left the table. The third was more friendly. A pale, stooped man of about fifty, with a long, lugubrious face. In spite of his sad expression he spoke frequently, imparting information and gossip.

When the others left the table, he gestured after them: "Air Force types. We have a lot of them here. Poor fellows are shell-shocked from the war." He shook his head. "I used to be a clergyman. Rev. Thompson."

Ronald looked appropriately respectful.

"I don't wear the collar any more so don't bother with the formalities. Just call me Algy."

"All right, Algy," said Ronald. He liked this eccentric-looking man. Creighton Hall was full of interesting people.

After dinner, Algy said he would conduct Ronald on a guided tour.

"These are the therapy areas," he said, and opened a door. Inside, Ronald saw a spacious room filled with all kinds of machinery.

"It's a sort of workshop, really," said Algy. "Are you clever with your hands?"

"I can make rugs," said Ronald.

"Admirable," said Algy. Suddenly he leaped to one side, ducked on his haunches, then leaped upward.

"Look out!" he cried. "It's after me again!" He ran full tilt down the corridor, weaving and bobbing like a rugby player, his thin legs flying.

Ronald stared after him. What was all that about? He saw Algy turn the corner with an incredibly acrobatic bound. Ronald ran down the corridor, after Algy, his curiosity aroused. As he neared the bend, Algy reappeared. He had stopped his gyrations but he looked distinctly apprehensive as though hiding from something hostile. Ronald gaped at him open-mouthed. He didn't know whether he should ask questions or not.

"It's electricity!" said Algy, his eyes darting in all directions. "It pursues me, you know. Comes out of light sockets. Always when I least expect it."

He wiped his forehead with a handkerchief.

"It's a unique condition, if I say so myself."

"How ... how does it ... er ... attack you, Algy?" asked Ronald, fascinated by the thought of electric rays pursuing people.

"It's a jagged blue streak," said Algy. "Leaps out of plugs and sockets and light bulbs too. I daren't close my eyes or it will get me for certain."

He put the moist handkerchief back in his pocket.

"I made them take all the electrical fittings out of my room," he said. "Couldn't take a chance of falling asleep. I've got candles now."

For the rest of the evening Algy was his normal, garrulous self. Ronald walked with him to his bedroom. Inside there were several candles burning, casting a soft yellow light.

"Well, good night, Ronald, see you tomorrow." Algy closed the door with a last nervous glance down the corridor at the light bulb in the ceiling.

Ronald walked off, to his own bed. It had been an exciting and interesting day. Such unusual people! Algy was definitely eccentric though, the way he ducked and dived around the place, dodging electricity. Ronald got into bed, read for a while, then fell asleep.

The next day Ronald was called to Dr Collingworth's office. When he entered, Dr Collingworth was polishing his glasses. He peered short-sightedly at Ronald.

"Enjoying yourself, I trust?"

"Oh yes, sir," said Ronald.

"Made any friends yet?"

Ronald told him about Admiral Henderson and Algy. Dr Collingworth smiled.

"It's a pity there's no one of your age here at the moment. All older people, some of them a lot older. But by all accounts that doesn't bother you overmuch."

"No, sir," said Ronald.

"I believe you are gambler," said the doctor.

"Yes, sir," said Ronald.

They spoke perfunctorily about gambling but the doctor didn't seem particularly interested in Ronald's complaint. He made it clear that he was a racegoer himself.

"The only sensible attitude to gambling is not to do too much of it," he said, a quick smile transforming his features.

"Do you masturbate often, Ronald?" said the doctor, peering at him.

"What, sir?" said Ronald, covered in confusion.

"Masturbate," he said.

"No, sir, I don't do anything like that," lied Ronald.

"No one admits it and everyone does it," said the psychiatrist wearily. He stood up. "All right Ronald, I don't think we'll have to see you again. We've hundreds of really serious cases here. A mild gambling compulsion is very small beer, really, when weighed against that sort of thing.

"I enjoy a little flutter myself," he said as he ushered Ronald from his office.

After he had been in his new environment for a few weeks, Ronald re-developed restlessness, the familiar feeling of anxious excitement. His compulsion to gamble was upon him again. He needed the optimism before a bet, the elation when he won, the despair and acceptance when he lost. Life was unbearably dull without this emotional catharsis. He began to make enquiries among the inmates. They showed interest. Ronald opened a book-making business in a small way. At first he took bets on the snooker knock-out tournament among the patients. Then he extended his book to dog racing.

Finally he took bets on the horse races each Saturday. Practically everyone had a flutter with him, including the psychiatrists. Many of the patients fancied themselves as contenders for the snooker championship, and backed themselves against the other participants.

Ronald laid odds on the whole field, ranging from six to four to hundred to one. He made a fair amount of money, which proved useful when he dated nurses and took them to the dances in the nearby village. During the day, Ronald took an interest in the therapy classes and decided to make another rug. The other rug-makers all worked to a simple plan—green rugs with canvas backing. Ronald designed a rug which had a pattern of bottles, glasses, cocktail shakers and swizzle sticks, in brown, yellow and beige. It was an intricate pattern which required thought. The others considered Ronald's project too complex, but he was determined to be different.

As the weeks went by, Ronald realised that he was in an asylum not a sanatorium. Many of the patients were deeply disturbed, most of them suffering from traumatic war-time experiences. He enjoyed the 'therapy' classes. His compulsion to gamble was satisfied by the small-scale book-making he operated. The nurses were cheerful, healthy girls who satisfied his need for feminine companionship.

After several months, Ronald was called to the head psychiatrist, Dr Palfrey, the genial pipe-smoking man he had met when he first arrived. He'd seen very little of Dr Palfrey since then.

"Ah, there you are," said the psychiatrist as Ronald entered his office. "Sit down, please, sit down."

Dr Palfrey had a file in front of him.

"I see," and he gestured at the document, "that you've been with us for eight months."

"Yes, sir," said Ronald, wondering what this was leading to.

"I trust you've had a pleasant time?"

"Oh yes, sir," said Ronald, sincerely. "I've been very happy, thank you."

Palfrey rose, knocked his pipe and began to clean it. He sat on the edge of the desk. It was a conspiratorial gesture.

"The truth is, Ronald," he said, "you don't really belong here. We have many truly sick people here, as you know."

Ronald nodded. He knew very well, by now, what sort of people were patients.

"Everything is in short supply. We need every available inch of space, every bed, for very deserving cases. Therefore, it becomes doubly imperative that we discharge you."

Dr Palfrey re-filled his pipe and blew out a plume of smoke. He got up and began to pace around the room in his shambling, absent-minded way.

"You gamble, so do many people. I'm going to discharge you as fit and well."

Dr Palfrey stopped his pacing.

"You'll have a certificate declaring you sane! That's more than most people have!" He laughed at his psychiatric joke.

Ronald smiled. He had become attuned to black comedy during the eight months.

"In other words, Ronald, you are free to leave and you should not regard yourself as being mentally deranged in any way."

He paused, and fixed his slightly watery eyes on Ronald.

"Just try and keep that gambling instinct in check, otherwise it will destroy you." He stood up briskly. "Now I have other people I must see."

He walked Ronald to the door and shook his hand.

"We've spoken to your parents, of course," he said. "You'll be leaving this afternoon."

Ronald, caught unawares by this new development, spent the rest of the day saying his farewells—and balancing his books with his customers. He said goodbye to 'Admiral' Henderson, and to Algy. He found Dr Collingworth, and thanked him. He wasn't quite sure what he was thanking him for, but it seemed polite. Dr Collingworth and he had had a strictly bookie-punter relationship since that first talk.

Dr Collingworth echoed Palfrey's words. "Gambling's like anything else, young fellow. All right in moderation."

At home once more, Ronald found it difficult to adjust to normal life and freedom of movement, missing in an ordered institution. Eight months away from his parents had changed nothing. Over their first meal together the question of his immediate future was brought up. His father wanted Ronald to work for him.

"You did tell him that if he passed with distinctions he could go to university, Jake," said Sarah. "I'm sure that's what Ronald would prefer to do."

"You're right, Mum," said Ronald. He'd never spoken with more sincerity. Anything would be preferable to being forced to spend every day constantly under the surveillance of his capricious father.

Jake waved an arm imperiously. "Those examination results were a flash in the pan. How do I know he'll study at university? Do you realise how much it costs, a university education?" He shook his head at the thought of the enormous sum involved.

"What would you like to study, Ronald?" asked his mother, as though the thought had just occurred to her.

"Architecture," said Ronald.

"Architecture?" said Jake. He mused for a while. Architecture, he thought. It was a good profession. An artistic one with opportunity for public recognition. Ronald had an artistic flair. After all, he won that poster competition.

As though reading her husband's thoughts, Sarah said matter-of-factly: "He could even be famous."

Ronald looked at his parents. He'd acquired a questioning, analytical attitude since his stay in Creighton Royal. Perhaps the psychiatrists were hero figures and he had identified with them. Whatever it was, a quality of empathy —an ability to identify with other's thoughts—had developed. He'd said architecture, in reply to his mother. He might just as well have said commerce, sociology, or biology. His arbitrary choice of architecture, however, did the trick. His father agreed. Ronald would go to university.

Ronald had been at university for three months when he was invited to dinner by one of his senior lecturers, Tomlinson. Tomlinson was a ferrety man with bright eyes. He smoked incessantly, with jerky gestures. He came straight to the point.

"You have the making of an architect, you know, Marcus," he said.

"Oh, thanks," said Ronald, with irony.

"Only the makings, I said. At the moment I don't see any signs of it, if you know what I mean."

"No, I don't," said Ronald, bridling.

"Well, you have a flippant approach, do you not?" The cigarette moved jerkily, clouds of smoke rising.

"I don't quite follow," said Ronald.

"Come, come, my dear fellow, don't be deliberately obtuse. You must know you have a reputation as a show-off? Or an eccentric young man, whichever you prefer." He laughed.

"Drawing green cows on white fields," he said.

"Sketching designs without bricks." He laughed again.

"I suppose it's your way of flaunting the establishment. On the other hand it's bloody juvenile behaviour which doesn't do you any good, apart from getting you mentioned on the grapevine."

Tomlinson abandoned the light-hearted manner which had characterised his conversation.

"I'm taking the trouble to tell you, Marcus, that you could be an architect if you tried. But the way you are going, you'll not last the first year."

Ronald felt that he'd missed the point of Tomlinson's remarks. But he nodded ... a neutral gesture. Tomlinson gave a snort and poured himself another drink. He didn't invite Ronald to dinner again.

About this time Ronald struck up a friendship with a student called Harry Potter, scion of a wealthy family. By his own admission he was 'going through the motions' at university. His real interests were girls, sports cars, and gambling. It was their mutual passion for a flutter which cemented the friendship between Ronald and Harry.

One day Potter discovered that Ronald had never been to a horse race meeting. He was dumbfounded.

"You've never been to the races?" Potter was tall, blond and effusive. "We'll have to rectify that." He thought for a moment.

"Newmarket! That's the ticket!"

Ronald laughed. "But that's three hundred miles away."

"I have my car," said Potter grandly.

"Yes, but you're forgetting something," said Ronald, amused. "Petrol." It was the immediate post-war period and petrol was virtually unobtainable.

"Harry Potter never admits defeat! I'll think of something. We'll be at Newmarket next weekend."

Potter did think of something. Money was no object. He and Ronald went on a shopping expedition. Using Harry's money they purchased 140 bottles of lighter fuel which they poured into Harry's sports car. They covered the three hundred miles to Newmarket without incident.

The two-day meeting at Newmarket featured first, the

1,000 Guineas race for three-year-old fillies and on the second day the main event, the 2,000 Guineas race for three-year-old colts. It was a panorama of colour, painted on a grander canvas than anything Ronald had seen at the dog-tracks. The horses, snorting in the paddock, and the stylish clothes created a sense of occasion. Ronald felt this was a setting for resounding triumph. The sport of kings! Potter took him around the course, explaining everything.

"How much money have you?" asked Potter casually.

"Thirty shillings," said Ronald. It was a pittance.

Potter looked taken aback.

"Well, anyway, follow my advice and perhaps you can build up a bank roll. The sensible thing is to back favourites. The favourite is the horse which expert opinion fancies, taking into consideration its breeding, performance, jockey, trainer and so on. Therefore, the favourite pays the shortest odds. Sometimes a favourite is so fancied that you virtually have to buy money—you may have to put on six pounds to win four."

"Buying money doesn't seem very exciting!" said Ronald.

"Perhaps not," said Potter. "But it's the intelligent way to bet."

Ronald followed his friend's advice and for the first three races, backed the favourite. In each case, it won.

Ronald counted his winnings. "Look at that!" he said, excitedly. "I've made fifteen pounds. Not bad, from a thirty bob start!"

Potter laughed. "You'll be rolling in the stuff by the time the meeting's over!"

The next day Ronald was so eager to feel the atmosphere of the race course again that he arrived well before the meeting was scheduled to start. He left Harry Potter at the hotel.

"You must be crazy," said Potter. "There'll be nothing happening for hours."

Ronald went ahead anyway, and enjoyed himself strolling around the course, mentally anticipating the excitements ahead. Fifteen pounds he'd won the day before. Who could say what fantastic sums he might transform it into before the day was over? Potter had told him that in the main race of the day, the 2,000 Guineas, there was a horse which was unbeatable.

"Dante is the most magnificent horse in the world," said Potter. "He's never been defeated. Don't waste your money trying to find anything to beat him. No matter how short the price, put all your money on Dante."

Somehow, Ronald regarded the backing of favourites as unexciting. It made gambling mundane. But as a novice, he decided to take his friend's advice. Harry Potter arrived, in good time for the first race. They placed their bets and for the first races their policy proved as successful as on the previous day. Ronald's roll of notes grew. Finally, the big event approached. The 2,000 Guineas. Potter and Ronald watched the horses parade. Dante was a striking animal, but to Ronald's untrained eye *all* the horses seemed superb.

He wandered among the book-makers, studying prices. Dante was even money favourite. The rest of the field were at long prices. It was clear that the entire racing fraternity regarded Dante as the only horse in the race. Ronald experienced a surge of revolt against the inflexibility of the system. This is ridiculous! he thought. Favourites can't always win. Surely there's more to horse racing that that! He decided, on impulse, to find something to beat the unbeatable Dante. He settled on a horse called Court Martial, a ten to one shot.

He and Harry stationed themselves near the finish.

"What price did you get?" asked Harry.

"Ten to one," said Ronald.

"Ten to one! What lunatic bookie gave you that?" cried Potter.

"Not Dante," said Ronald. "Court Martial." He hadn't wanted to admit his refusal to accept his friend's advice until after the race was over.

"You've backed something else! That's throwing your

money away!" said Potter. He shook his head. "Oh well. You'll have to learn the hard way."

"How much do you have on Dante?" asked Ronald.

"A hundred," said Potter.

"Can I borrow your binoculars?" asked Ronald. Harry passed them to him. Ronald adjusted them and scanned the course. An electric clock came into his field of vision. He was reminded of the cracks in the canal when he was a child. If you step on the cracks, you lose. If you miss the cracks everything will be all right. The digits on the clock face changed as the minutes went by.

Ronald had the absolute conviction that if he kept looking at the clock until it changed to the next digit, Court Martial would win the race. If his glance strayed, and he didn't see the change, the horse would lose. He held the glasses firmly, his eyes watering with the intensity of his stare, until the digit clicked over. He sighed with relief and handed the binoculars back to Harry.

The horses came under the starter's orders, then they were off. The voice of the commentator echoed through the speakers. Dante figured prominently in the commentary. Gradually the level of excitement in the voice rose until the words were a torrent, just coherent.

"Court Martial!" Ronald heard his horse's name mentioned. "Neck and neck with Dante." He glanced at Potter, who gave a look of unfeigned astonishment.

The two horses came charging down the straight and hurtled past them, foam flying from their nostrils, sweat pouring from their haunches. To Ronald's inexperienced eye it seemed impossible to decide the winner but he felt the impact of Potter's fist on his shoulder.

"You've won!" he shouted. "Beginner's luck, that's what it is!"

Dazed, Ronald looked about him. The crowd seemed stunned, standing in silent disbelief. The mighty Dante had been defeated. The racing certainty of all time. An angry buzz of conversation broke out. The commentator's voice, restored to normal tones after the excitement, announced the official result, Court Martial, by a short head from

Dante. In the remaining races, Ronald returned to a conservative betting pattern and won. He had accumulated £165.

He and Potter were comparing their winnings when a man dashed up to Potter. His name was Williams. He and Potter were racing pals. Harry had told Ronald that Williams had access to inner circles of racing. He knew jockeys and trainers, as well as stewards. His information was from the horse's mouth. He was telling Potter about the big race.

"It happened at the 'off'. A stone flew into Dante's right eye, blinding him. Isn't that fantastic? Blind and ran second. What a horse! Don't breathe a word," he said, his eyes flashing with excitement. "Here's the chance of a coup," and he dashed off again.

Potter explained: "Dante's price is going to lengthen for the Derby because of his defeat. But we know why he was beaten—he would have won if it hadn't been for that stone."

They made their way past the bookies, who were calling the odds for the Derby.

"Ten to one, Dante," a bookie shouted.

"Right," said Ronald. He produced £150 and placed it on Dante to win.

As he took his ticket, Potter looked at him admiringly.

"For someone who arrived with thirty bob you've turned into a real plunger," he said. "Ten to one! If Dante makes it, you'll win £1,650."

They began the long drive home. Ronald felt impatient. The Derby would not be run for two months. As Potter drove, Ronald thought back on his first experience of horse racing. It had been exciting, dramatic, alive. He felt frustration. He couldn't wait for the next opportunity to gamble . . . and win again.

In the next few weeks several changes took place in Ronald's life. He left university after being refused permission to take his first-year examinations. The atmosphere with his parents was unbearable. His father ceaselessly crowed over the accuracy of his prediction that Ronald would drop out of university.

Ronald left home and obtained a job as an assistant at a multiple tailors in a distant city. He lived in digs. He had no money. The few pounds left after Newmarket races had been frittered at the dogs. Now that he'd severed his tie with his parents he had no allowance. He managed on a small wage from his job. It was dreary. Now, when Ronald had a bet, it was in shillings and that was only possible on the day he received his wages.

But Ronald had one shining hope. He still had £150 on Dante for the Derby. As the race day neared Ronald tried to raise enough money to go to Epsom, but he was unsuccessful. He would have to listen to the race on the radio. Alone in his small room, Ronald crouched beside the old fashioned set, his ear to the speaker.

"They're off!" cried the commentator. Ronald crushed out his cigarette in anticipation.

As the voice described the race, Ronald's excitement reached fever pitch.

"Dante is lying sixth, with only three furlongs to go," said the imperturbable voice.

Sixth! Had the jockey judged it right? he wondered.

"Dante is moving smoothly on the outside ..."

Ronald felt a pounding tension in his head.

"Into the last furlong," said the voice, building to a higher pitch.

"Dante's being given a tap with the whip. It's incredible!" the commentator's voice broke with hysteria.

"Dante is sailing home! I don't know how to describe this, it's unbelievable, what a horse! Dante is winning the Derby as he wants to ..."

There was a brief pause as the commentator regained his composure.

"It's all over. Dante has won."

Ronald sat at the radio, motionless. He had won £1,650. A fortune! £1,650. But his elation was followed by a curiously empty feeling.

Ronald collected his winnings from the bookmakers.

Somehow the money didn't mean much. Anyway, he thought, with everything in such short supply, there's nothing to spend it on. The next day he went to the cinema. The newsreel started and Ronald was riveted. It was the Derby. The scene of his victory! He leaned forward in his seat. The camera had captured every moment of the great race. Ronald relived the thrilling climax, as the long-striding champion horse incredibly swept past the rest of the field. When it was over, he sat through the main film, his thoughts still on that wonderful moment.

Ronald returned to the cinema six times. During his first excited viewing something had escaped him. He wanted to see the action again and again. Finally he saw what he was looking for. The attention of everyone, including the film cameramen, had been on Dante's startling finish, but Ronald now had a fleeting glimpse of another horse. It came rocketing from far behind the others to finish sixth. Dante was striding out, but this mystery horse was travelling even faster than Dante. Ronald was able to make out the horse's number. He checked it. Naishapur, a complete outsider. After seeing the newsreel for the sixth time, Ronald weighed up the racing situation. The next big race on the calendar was the St Leger, run over a mile and threequarters, quarter of a mile longer than the Derby. The extra distance would favour Naishapur.

When the betting opened on the St Leger, Dante was even money favourite. Other fancied horses were Court Martial and Midas.

Naishapur was thiry-three to one.

Ronald made his decision. He took £1,500 and went to a bookmaker.

"£750 each way Naishapur." The bookie wrote the ticket, his eyebrows raised.

Now that the wager was made, Ronald experienced his customary feeling of impatience. But there was no hurrying the course of strange events which now took place.

Next morning, Ronald bought a newspaper and turned to the sporting section. He read that Naishapur had been backed from thirty-three to one down to twenty to one.

"What luck!" he thought. "I managed to get thirty-three to one just in time."

It did not occur to him that *his* £750 each way had shortened the odds. Some time later Dante was withdrawn from the St Leger and put to stud. The champion not competing shortened the odds on the remaining horses.

Naishapur came down in the betting to twelve to one. Then, Court Martial was also withdrawn. Again, odds shortened on the remaining competitors. Next, Midas was scratched.

Naishapur descended to three and a half to one.

On Leger day, Ronald and Harry Potter were at the course. Potter was more excited than Ronald. He missed no opportunities to talk of Ronald's remarkable betting coup. Naishapur, the present favourite, at thirty-three to one—a £750 each way bet! It was phenomenal.

By now the field had been reduced to only a few horses. Naishapur was the seven to four *on* favourite.

Ronald would win whether Naishapur ran first, second or third, out of five runners.

He and Potter waited for the race to start. Now, Ronald had his own binoculars and he went through what had become a routine—watching the electric totalisator. The numbers flickering and changing as they reflected the ebb and flow of the betting. The hypnotic fascination of the altering figures held him rigidly. Don't look away! an inner voice said. If you miss the movement of the numbers everything will go wrong. As he watched, a new digit tumbled into place. He brought the glasses down, relieved.

There was a clang and they were 'off'. Only five horses competing in one of the world's great races. The field was bunched for most of the race. Then, at the turn into the final stretch, there was a mêlée of bumping and jostling. Ronald searched for Naishapur's colours as the horses came thundering past. He saw them. Naishapur was last. He turned to Harry and they exchanged a look of incredulity.

If Naishapur had won, Ronald would have collected

212

£34,000. Now, he was penniless once again. Ronald felt the coldness of financial insecurity. His hopes had been dashed. He thought of his job at the tailors, working long hours every day for a bare living. The future looked grim.

Twenty-five years passed. Ronald was forty-five. His hair was flecked with grey. Behind him lay two marriages. He had two children, both of them at university.

Forty-five is a contemplative time of life. Ronald looked back on the years. He had made great sums of money in various enterprises. He had also sustained enormous gambling losses. Although he gambled obsessively he had always met his obligations as a husband and a father. His gambling compulsion created anxiety for himself—but his family had been spared the consequences.

He remembered his first marriage. There had been no wedding present from his father. His mother gave a gift 'from your father and me'. But Ronald knew it was from his mother alone. It was the same when he married again. When his first son was born, Ronald's father created a scene a few days prior to the expected birth. As a result, he never saw his grandson for the first year of his life.

The emotional warfare had continued into Ronald's middle years. Only recently, father and son had been locked in bitter dispute. Disillusionment upset Ronald still as he recalled the incident. His father had said to him: "You're doing well. You have a mortgage of £7,000 on your house. Let me help you. I'll take over the mortgage. Instead of paying eleven per cent, as you are doing, pay me five per cent and I'll never ask you for the capital."

Six months later, Ronald decided to leave Britain. His second marriage had collapsed and he had no desire to remain in familiar surroundings.

He found a buyer for his house and approached his father in the routine procedure of a transfer of documents. As the holder of the mortgage, his father had been entrusted with the deeds. Ronald's solicitor required them in order to conclude the sale.

His father refused. He said he would not part with the deeds until he had the £7,000 in cash.

Ronald's mother had pleaded. "After all," she'd said, "it's normal to sell the house then arrange the payment."

Jake shook his head.

"But, Father," said Ronald, "I have to leave the country in three days. Be reasonable."

Jake Marcus was adamant. He would not part with the deeds until he had the cash in his hand.

Ronald in cold anger left his father. When he returned thirty-six hours later he had sold other assets and he had £7,000 in cash, plus a court order available to demand the release of the deeds. Even then, Jake fought a delaying action, claiming that the documents were in a safe at his solicitors. But finally he had to capitulate.

Ronald remembered both his wives. He always had a deeply ingrained mistrust of women. He had not trusted his wives ... and they had proved by their actions that they were not trustworthy. But could he say with truth that his lack of trust had not pushed them into situations of betrayal? He could not.

His past was full of achievements in which he could take pride, but it was also devastated by the consequences of his gambling. Whatever he had built, gambling had torn down. The pendulum of luck swung from elation to despair, security to anxiety, high hopes to shattered plans. What now? he thought. What lies ahead? Would the destructive pattern continue?

CLINICAL DIAGNOSIS (1)
by: Dr Bernard Levinson, MB, BCH, DPM

I have two images of Ronald. There is the young boy of the story, and the mature adult that I have met. My meeting with Ronald was dramatic. The curtain opens, the stage is darkened, an attractive young woman holds the centre and sparkles in the spotlight. The audience is hushed and she introduces Ronald. Ronald takes immediate possession of the stage and the entire audience. He is warm, confidential and totally in control. His conversation is easy and relaxed, and one tends to forget that he is performing essentially alone on the stage. For all of us, time has stopped and we are hanging on to his words. When he has been on the stage for only a few minutes, we are all, in a sense, in a trance.

It's difficult to see the Ronald of the story in the Ronald of the stage. The Ronald who stands before his parents, repeating the awful words after his father, "I am a terrible liar" and "I told my father I had a shilling and I have spent it all on sweets". Humiliated before his mother and before his father. Angry with them both and totally impotent before them.

The psychopathology of gambling is extremely complex. Somewhere at the basic core of the gambler, there is the need to fail, followed by the need to be punished, to be chided and abused. Followed in turn by their being forgiven, with a promise that they will never again gamble. Ronald's upbringing prepares him in many ways for this sinister drama that must be endlessly repeated. His father plays a destructive game of "let me double your money". There is the promise of love, parental support and reassurance, followed inevitably by a hopeless sense of desolation.

Either the prize is not forthcoming when he has fulfilled his end of the bargain, or he has, wittingly or not, entered into a contract with father in which father's offer to 'double the money' ends in a total débâcle with Ronald being humiliated and abused. The episode in which he is taken down the stairs, through the kitchen, into the back garden where his mother sat reading, and was then degraded in her presence, is an example of this.

The soaring feelings of optimism that Ronald experiences before each race have their roots in his earliest relationships with father. These are father's overtures that awaken a sense of fulfilment in Ronald: "Let me help you; be my son; let me be your father; let us do things together—let me double your money . . ."

215

The elation of winning is short-lived and frequently absent. Winning more frequently leaves a sense of hollowness and despair. This is comparable to finally handing father the bank book, with the five pounds ostensibly intact. There is, in fact, no way of satisfying father. There is no way of winning.

The relationship between father and son is extremely punitive and destructive. Ronald, again and again exposes himself to father's destructive game, and again and again he is betrayed. The Christmas stocking filled with rubbish must have overwhelmed the child with a sense of defeat and rejection. This could only leave him with a feeling of "I must be bad". "This could only happen to me if I were bad. If I were good, people would love me. But my parents can't love me; they send me to school and abandon me so that I am the only child left in school during the holidays. I am taken to hospital because there is something inside me that is sick and bad."

All efforts to please father, such as to make money or attain status, either fail miserably or have no meaning when finally achieved. All attempts at being 'good' turn to utter helplessness. Mother, who must have initially given the young child love and protection, is gradually drawn to father's side, and in turn cannot be trusted. Women, as a consequence, would have to be controlled and treated with suspicion. They would always be capable of betraying and would always have to be watched. Ronald as a child emerges subtly within the adult who has to control his wife, lest she abandon him.

Early in his life, Ronald develops obsessive, compulsive symptoms. He has to avoid cracks, to avert disasters. He has to watch the second hand of the clock through his binoculars, or he will lose the race. He has to rely on magic, because nothing can be trusted to go his way. Relationships will have to be controlled. A marriage could only be successful if there was sufficient predictability and security.

The curtain rises, and I am slowly made aware that the need to vindicate an entire childhood can provide one with the most powerful need to succeed and that this can be translated into a tremendously creative force. I am watching 'Romark', the highly polished entertainer, and I am strongly aware how his charm binds us to him.

CLINICAL DIAGNOSIS (2)
by: Ronald Markham (Romark)

As Dr Levinson has already divulged, the compulsive gambler in 'Double or Nothing' is the author of this book —Ronald Markham.

Although I am about to give a clinical diagnosis of my own case, I shall do this objectively as with the other diagnoses.

The source of Ronald's problems was his father—Jake Marcus. Jake's behaviour, in turn, was created by *his* parents, who deprived him of love and warmth. Jake, as a youngster, was starved of love—a need which he fulfilled when he married Sarah. Sarah gave him affection, and it became vital to Jake that his wife should regard him as important (even though his sense of inadequacy allowed him no true self-esteem).

Jake did not want anything to interrupt his idyllic life with Sarah and he was angry when they had their baby. Ronald was an only child—the sole recipient of Sarah's motherly love.

Jake resented this strongly. Sarah's attention and affection were diverted from him to their son. He began to compete with Ronald for his wife's attention. He felt robbed of his full entitlement of love. He would rip a button off his coat, then ask Sarah to stitch it on for him. As she sat next to him, repairing, he would bask in her full attention. He would invent friendships with important people (the newspaper editor, the City Councillor) in a bid to make himself important to his wife.

Jake's competitive attitude towards his son caused Ronald to become a compulsive gambler. Gambling is self-destructive. The compulsive gambler deludes himself that he gambles to win. Logic, however, tells him that he cannot. He is surrounded by visible proof of this—prosperous bookmakers, stadiums, race courses and gambling boom towns. In any gambling operation it is not the punter who makes the profit, but the operator. Obviously, therefore, the compulsive gambler actually bets to lose. The purpose of this investigation is to discover the source of that compulsion.

Ronald had an early recollection of sharing a penny ice with a friend. This was the first time he was forced to worry about money. It was a money-equals-worry situation. In this first 'worry' we have the halving of an ice. To halve an object which creates two equal portions, is the same as doubling it.

The next money-worry was when Uncle Leon gave Ronald a shilling which he spent. When father badgered him, Ronald pretended he had it locked away. His father then used an inducement—"I'll double your money," he said. When he had completed his persecution of Ronald and proved that the money had been spent, he took Ronald to the reformatory. This situation imprinted on the boy's mind an association between money worries and real or imagined crimes.

The Christmas stocking was a deliberate cruelty. The money worry in this case being the pretence that there had been a five-pound note among the rubbish. By this time Ronald had passed his formative years. He was now thirteen. Already his character was formed destructively towards gambling.

Ronald now knew that the only way to obtain his father's attention was to have money worries. He created them by gambling. His first gamble was on the seaside penny-machines, when he was on holiday.

When he rolled that first penny in a bid to double his money, he knew, subconsciously, that his father would eventually refer to his bank book and ask what had become of the contents. That was the reason Ronald kept the savings book with him. He needed it to be available so that it could play its role in his recurring playlet of attention getting. When Ronald drew the money out of the bank, he knew he was creating another money-worry.

Rolling that first penny, the resultant persecution-by-mail, the grief, the hard work on the farm to make up the money—all these occurrences, were preconceived in Ronald's subconscious. He *knew* he was creating financial anxiety—which would focus his father's attention on him, albeit critically.

When Ronald painted the prize-winning poster, he actually believed that he had gained his father's attention without a money worry. When father offered him a reward he didn't want it. He only wanted father's interest. Ronald did not get his reward. Again he was a loser. A money-worry situation was also created when the school house-keeper asked Ronald to buy soap powder and he didn't have the money. He gambled—this time by stealing. He gambled on whether he would be caught or not. As usual he lost the gamble.

When Ronald went to Edinburgh and his Uncle Robert took him to the greyhound track, he was happier than he had ever been. He received love and attention from his relatives which ameliorated his self-destructive impulses. Because of this, he did not bet with characteristic reckless-ness—and he won.

Before the school examinations, his father offered the usual inducements. "Double your money"—twenty-five pounds for a pass, fifty pounds for a distinction. Ronald didn't want the money, he didn't want bribes. He wanted attention. At this point Ronald was beginning to realise that he could not get love from his father because it did not exist. He knew he was hitting his head against a brick wall but still compulsively tried to achieve the impossible. Ronald passed his examinations, but his father did not give him either the financial reward promised, or attention —Ronald lost again.

When Ronald stole his father's silver cigarette box, it was a perfect example of his compulsion to seek attention. It was inevitable that the theft would be discovered instantly—and Ronald knew this. Moving into his own lodgings locked Ronald out of the family circle. His exclusion from his father's approval was emphasised. He lost the rent money—symbolically drawing attention to his not being within the family.

Even when Ronald was sent to an asylum, he still tried to convince himself of his father's love. He refused naïvely, for a boy of his age, to accept that he was among lunatics. He persisted in regarding them as eccentrics, accepting his parents' explanation that it was a "rest home for people with nerves". He could not bring himself to believe that his father would commit him to such a place.

When Ronald went to university, he effectively destroyed his chances through behaviour motivated by two impulses. He did not believe himself to be any good (how could he be, when his own father didn't like him?). And he sought attention by misguidedly cultivating the pose of an eccentric exhibitionist.

The pattern of the compulsive gambler is illustrated by the horse-racing episode in which Ronald parlayed thirty shillings into £1,650 and then gambled virtually the whole amount on Naishapur. The horse lost—but if it had won, and Ronald had collected £34,000, he would have immediately wagered it on some other horse in a bid to win a million. As long as he won he would have continued betting—until he achieved his real objective, which was to lose.

The later episode concerning the house mortgage demonstrated that even at the age of forty-five, Ronald was still saying to his father: I believe you love me. I'll give you the mortgage on my house so that you can look after me. The trouble which resulted was a predictable manifestation of his father's continuing behaviour, which Ronald knew, subconsciously, would take place.

Here, in this clinical diagnosis, we have a perfect example of how the human mind can cheat. I have been saying throughout this book that the mind is a deceiver and a trickster. Although, I believed this when I said it,

I was granting myself the power of being different, in that I knew myself, as others could not know themselves.

I confess I am no different from anyone else. Over the years I rationalised my gambling by thinking that I did it in an attempt to become richer and more powerful than my father. But I have not mentioned this explanation in the clinical diagnosis, because it is not true.

Let me explain. This book was written by dictating the information for each story and each clinical diagnosis into a tape recorder in haphazard sequence. Another person sorted out the order and typed the stories. Then in each case I went through the stories, making alterations. This working pattern was used throughout the book. But when it came to *my* story, the gambler, I read it objectively, as if it were about someone else. I then realised that the original (unused) clinical diagnosis did not make sense.

I rewrote the clinical diagnosis in the form you have just read. As I put the corrected facts on to paper, I became emotionally upset with the realisation that I was *now* telling the truth about myself, instead of a rationalised fiction. I experienced a shocking sensation, torrents of tears, and I felt a lifetime of worry and strain connected with money and gambling being washed away.

From that moment I knew that I had no wish to gamble at any time in the future.

I knew I was cured. This happened one year before the publication of the book and I am still free from any gambling compulsion. No effort is required on my part *not to gamble*—I am *not interested* in gambling any more.

My cure could have been caused by a combination of unusual circumstances. Maybe at the age of forty-five I achieved emotional maturity and decided to discard my father and cure myself—or perhaps it was a miracle.

But I am certain the cure is permanent and that I will never again be haunted by the desire to 'Double my money'.

Romark continues his chronicle of 'the sins of the fathers' in *The Curse of the Children*. If you have not found your own problem analysed in this volume, then you will find it among the nine stories which the author tells in *The Curse of the Children*, also published by Coronet Books.